Transexed and Transgendered People
A Guide

Also edited by the author:
The Gendys Conference Reports,
1990, 1992, 1994, 1996, 1998, 2000, 2002, 2004
as organiser and contributor.

Network website:
http://www.gender.org.uk/gendys/index.htm

Transexed and Transgendered People A Guide

For those needing guidance,
those seeking to understand,
and those concerned with their care and treatment.

Alice Purnell

GENDYS NETWORK
2004

TRANSEXED AND TRANSGENDERED PEOPLE
A GUIDE

For those needing guidance, those seeking to understand,
and those concerned with their care and treatment.

Alice Purnell

Copyright 2004
ISBN 0 9525107 7 4

I Alice Purnell, hereby assert and give notice of my right under Section 77 of the Copyright, Designs and Patents Act 1988 to be identified as the author of this work.

Published by GENDYS Conferences
BM GENDYS, London WC1N 3XX

British Library Cataloguing-in-Publication Data.
A catalogue record for this book
is available from the British Library.

Produced by the Derby TV/TS Group, Belper, Derby, England.
Printed by Intype Libra Ltd
Units 3-4, Elm Grove Industrial Estate Wimbledon, London SW19 4HE

CONTENTS.

Chapter

Page

1. Introduction. 9
2. Terminology 11
3. Discussion: Sex, Sexual Identity, Gender and Sexual Preference.
  How does this Dysphoria arise? 17
4. Incidence. 19
5. Cross Gender Manifestations - the Gender Spectrum. 19
6. A Question of Identity. 21
7. How Sexual Identification is Established. 22
8. So What Makes a Person, is it Nature or is it Nurture? 23
9. Aetiology …The origins of gender dysphoria. 23
10. A Cure? and Why "Change Sex"? 28
11. Natural Variations. 29
12. Stereotypes. 30
13. Boys will be Boys. 32
14. Humans are Not Particularly Sexually Dimorphic. 33
15. Women in a Man's World. 34
16. Variation is Natural. 35
17. Sex, Like Gender, is Not Dipolar. 36
18. Attitudes of Society. 38
19. Religious and Ethical Questions. 39
20. Those who Oppose Equality for "T people". 41
21. Guilt Trips. 43
22. Transgendered Behaviour in History and Biography. 44
23. Difficulties and Practicalities of Change. 47
24. Order in a World where Gender or Sexual Polarity
  Cannot Clearly divide People. 49
25. Passing successfully male to female (MtF). 50
  a) Voice 51
  b) Body Language. 51
  c) Electrolysis and facial and body hair. Laser Treatment 51
26. Passing successfully female to male (FtM). 54
  a) Voice. 54
  b) Height. 55
  c) Bodyshape. 55
27. Where To Get Help - How to Cope with Legal and Administrative Matters. 55
28. To Formalise a Name Change using a Statutory Declaration. 57
29. Other Documents. 57
  a) Medical Card/Records. 57
  b) Income Tax Files and Records 59
  c) Bank Accounts/Post Office/Building Society
  Savings Accounts/Share Certificates 59

d) Pensions. 59

e) National Insurance Office and DSS files. 59

f) Driving Licence. 59

g) Utilities and Insurance Companies. 59

h) Electoral Registration. 60

i) Property. 60

j) Life and Medical Insurance. 60

k) A caution for Divorcees. 60

l) Exam Certificates 60

m) Passports. 60

n) A Will and other Loose Strands. 60

30. Relationships. 61

31. Marriage and a Transperson - (If Marriage was Before Change-over). 65

32. Children of a Transperson. 66

33. Counselling - How Then, Can the Therapist or
Counsellor Help her/his Client? 69

34. What is the Role, Purpose or Goal of Counselling? 69

35. The Need for Personal Therapy and Counselling. 70

36. The NHS and Private Medicine/Psychiatry
Few Resources and Long Waiting Lists. 72

37. Funding Problems and Consequences. 72

38. Age and the Constraints of Chronology. 73

39. Who Do We Blame? 74

40. So what do I mean by Difference and the Existential? 75

41. Recommendations on the Level of Care. 76

42. There is a Problem in Treating Identity by Medical Means. 78

43. No Person should be Forced to Live a Lie 79

44. Care Standards as Opposed to Standards of Care. 81

45. There are still Failures in Care and Casualties of the Treatments Available. 82

46. Gender Counselling and its Difficulties in Cases of Acute and Chronic G.D. 83

47. Two Atypical Clients 83

48. The So-called "Real Life Test" and Employment. 95

49. The Standards of Care (SOC) for Hormonal and
Surgical Reassignment of G.D. Persons. 98

50. Gender Identity Clinics (GIC's) - Charing Cross Hospital. 100

51. Hormones (MtF) 103

52. Hormones (FtM). 109

53. Considerations Surrounding Hormones. 110

54. The Non-Surgical Solution … Living Transgendered. 114

55. Gender Reassignment Surgery (GRS). 115

The "Cosmetic" Operation. 115

Vaginoplasty. 115

Clitoroplasty 115

Drop-pedicle Colon Graft 115

Pre-operative precautions. 117

Post-operative care. 118

56. Surgery MtF - Outcome and Prognosis. 120

57. Orchidectomy. 123

58. Surgery (FtM). 125

    1. Mastectomy. 125

    2. Hysterectomy. 125

    3. Phalloplasty. 125

    4. Scrotoplasty 126

59. Some Cosmetic Options 127

Mammoplasty. Breast enlargement, 127

Rhinoplasty (Nose reshaping). 128

Reduction of the Adam's Apple. 128

60. Social Changeover. 128

61. Diversity and Respect. 130

62. Trans people, Language and the Legal Mess. 132

63. The Legal Block to Full Acceptance

          Prior to the Gender Recognition Act (2004). 134

a) The Birth Certificate 135

b) Marriage. 136

c) Rape. 136

d) Pensions. 137

e) National Insurance. 137

f) Divorce. 137

g) Maintenance. 137

h) The anomaly of Testicular Feminization. 137

i) Offences during change over 138

The Public Order Act 1936 (sects 5 & 7). 138

j) Sex Discrimination Act. 139

k) Prison. 139

64. Since the Gerbil the Birth Certificate can be Amended in the U.K. 139

65. Press For Change 140

66. Identity Cards. 141

67. Civil Partnerships. 141

68 The Gender Recognition Act. 141

69. Over 50's Survey. 142

70. A Qualitative and Quantitative Survey of 102 Transpeople 1990/2 185

71. Parents and their Gender Dysphoric/ Transexed Child. 213

72. Supporting the Families of Adult Gender Dysphoric and Transsexual People. 216

73. Post Script - Standard Care? A Counsellor's Overview. 227

74. Bibliography and Further Reading. 236

Acknowledgements.

Many thanks are due to Jed Bland for his friendship, advice, and help with the layout this book, and the article, Section 53, on hormones.

Also to:

Dr. Dorothy Jerrome (50 + Survey).

Dr. Asscheman (Netherlands) for assistance with the passages on hormones and surgery.

Prof. John Money (USA) for quotes from the 'Gender Spectrum' and 'Criteria' H.B.I.G.D. Assn. Inc. (excerpts Standards of Care).

Thanks to the University of Sussex Post Graduate Medical Library.

Prof. Louis Gooren and to the Free University Hospital Gender Team in Amsterdam.

The late Judy Cousins, who provided the information on electrolysis.

Dr. Don Montgomery (UK) for permission to reproduce the Clinical Management Policy of the Charing Cross Hospital.

Rev. Canon Clinton Jones (USA) for some of the ideas on ethical questions.

Rev. David Horton for his support to the GENDYS community

Dr. Russell Reid (UK)

The late Dr. Roy Mottram.

Diana Aitchison (WOBS)

Janett Scott (Beaumont Society)

Terry and Bernard Reed for permission to include the GIRES Article

I also thank the late Claire Warren for providing half the red wine and laughter, over conversations in the good old days thirty years ago, as we were talking and thinking about how one might help, the need for this sort of book, but also of poetry, good friends and so much else.

Dedications.

This Book is dedicated to my wonderful daughters Sara and Rebecca.

Also to my late son Benedict, who died in 1997. He was a friend, had beautiful nature and played Piano Ragtimes so well. He was much loved and is so missed by our family and his friends.

This book is further dedicated to all those who search for the truth with a generosity of heart.

1. Introduction.

In my book *A Guide to Transsexualism, Transgenderism and Gender Dysphoria*, I produced a brief guide to these phenomena. In the light of the Gender Recognition Act it became necessary to provide a rewrite. This also presented an opportunity to expand the book and update much of the material. Since I have researched and presented many papers on these topics I believe that it might be better to include that material, together with updates on thinking and terminology since that book was printed (the latest Edition was in 1998. It is now out of print).

Working as a gender-counselling psychologist and for many years as a senior nurse, I was able to approach this topic from a medical and from a psychological perspective. Further, I have worked with the Trans community for thirty eight years, during which I have had the privilege of meeting hundreds of people in this predicament from the UK, Ireland, France, Netherlands, Belgium, Scandinavia, Iberia, India, Canada and the USA, together with professionals in the field of care for them.

Gender Dysphoria has involved a great deal of interest from various disciplines, psychology, counselling, psychiatry, surgery, endocrinology, genetics, sociology, gender studies, politics, law, speech therapy, laser treatment, electrology, employment, policing, housing, diversity groups, biography, and so on. Not withstanding this, the general public and indeed many professionals are completely ignorant of this phenomenon. Regarding Transsexualism, Transgenderism and Gender Dysphoria, there are more questions than answers. Surely the most important answer must be tolerance and understanding to and from the Gender Dysphoric person. Few who have not suffered from this will comprehend what it is like to be such a person. Each 'GD person' is different, each an individual in his or her own right, with an individual identity, experience and life course.

Most people's gender coincides with their announced sex at birth. The individual's self perception comes from within, as well as from 'messages' from others: "Is it a girl or a boy?" is the first question we ask of a baby. Usually that answer can be given with confidence, but it is apparent in physical terms that some are born without a clearly 'male' or 'female' body, hormonal balance or chromosomes. Gender can not be based solely on anatomy or chromosomes. This is physiologically evident, as in the case of intersexed children and hermaphrodites. In the case of the 'Trans' person there is discord - dysphoria - between the evidence of mind and of body. The body is out of step with the mind. It is a question of identity. Often there is no confusion, but an overwhelming conviction of personal gender, out of synch with the body and 'designated' life-course.

It seems there are some acceptable generalisations, but 'the answer is there is no absolute answer' concerning questions as to how and why this human behaviour arises. There are many theories as to the origin, which I attempt to explore here. What seems more important is to address how we should manage this, so as to enhance the life of the individual. Each individual's answer as to how they come to terms with this difficulty and find an acceptable way of being is within him or her self. Perhaps that is a counsellor's task, to enable the person to find a way of being, with damage limitation. It is an imperfect situation in a world that seems challenged by the gender transgression of the Transexed person. Ignorance and prejudice of Society have added to the sense of despair felt by many. There are also other people who find it difficult to come to terms with this situation, when a person, close to them, may be beset with this history. They also need understanding in a culture of blame. Partners, parents and family are often particularly challenged by this situation.

There is strong evidence that the "Benjamin Syndrome" (named after Prof. Harry Benjamin, including Gender Dysphoria, Transgenderism, Gender Identity Conflict, Transsexualism, or whatever label we give the symptoms), is a form of 'brain sex' intersexuality or duality or discord. It is probably more to do with the wiring of the brain than any subsequent behavioural or outside influences. It involves core identity rather than body chemistry, chromosomes, anatomy, or upbringing. Above all, respect, understanding and empathy are required of others around the transexed person. This book attempts to provide information. Individual responses to personal identity and life course problems require individual solutions and ways of being.

I include aspects of surgery and hormones for the professional in the field, since there is little such information collected in a single source. I also go into some depth regarding Counselling.

2. Terminology

A Chinese proverb says that the beginning of wisdom is giving things the right name.

The vocabulary we use can affect the way we think. It can cause great offence and be disrespectful if we use terms which insult people if they are not appropriate. It also can cause muddled thinking and confusion.

Before this text is approached it will be necessary to give some definitions. It is important to make a basic distinction between sex and gender.

Sex is a biological phenomenon; gender is a cultural one, with probable biological origin.

Definitions:

Sex in its simplest terms, concerning humans, can be defined as being a male or a female. It refers to a set of biological characteristics linked to reproduction. Sex is biological i.e. male or female. It *implies* you are a boy/man or a girl/woman.

Intersexed refers to a person whose sex is not clearly defined anatomically. There are chromosomal errors like Turner's Syndrome (where one of the XX or XY sex chromosomes is missing) and Klinefelter's Syndrome (XXY syndrome) or hermaphroditism where the anatomical sex has elements of both sexes.

Hermaphroditism (Intersex) A Hermaphrodite is a person whose sex is ambiguous (at birth). She or he does not have a gender dysphoria disorder as such. The actual gender identity may be female or male or intermediate.

Chromosomal abnormalities such as Turner's or Klinefelter's Syndromes, and hormonal response or lack of it, such as in Androgen Insensitivity Syndrome, Congentital Adrenal etc., can cause further variations from the norm. These variations have been seen as 'experiments of nature' which may ultimately throw some further light on the complex causes of variations of gender identity and these conditions.

There are also conditions where there have been developmental variants from the norm: like Hypospadias, Hypogonadism and Gynaecomastia. There are even some people who are born without visible anatomical sexual indicators.

It is now generally recognised that males and females do have vestiges of the other sex and a potential which includes elements of the other sex. Sex is in fact on a continuum. In humans there is actually relatively little sexual dimorphism, but a little bit makes a big difference as to how we see ourselves and others see us.

Sexual Identity is a sense of belonging to one sex or another.

There are seven criteria for establishing sexual identification defined by Prof. J. Money 1963.

(From a talk given at the London Institute.)

1 Chromosomal sex (normal male and normal female).
2 Gonadal Sex (Ovaries or testes).
3 Hormonal function
4 Internal genital morphology
5 External genital morphology
6 Assigned sex (at birth)
7 Psychosexual differentiation.

** I would add Brain Sex and interaction of the genetic material in the complexities of individual variation, which may affect gender identity.

Psychosexual Differentiation is how we are polarised towards one gender or another and is a psychological and sexual expression of that.

Sexual Preference is a person's preferred sex object or object of affection and is to do with sexuality not gender. Like the rest of society transsexuals may be heterosexual, bisexual, asexual or homosexual - transhomosexual* in this case.

*Dorothy Clare, Bryan Tully, Ph.D. (1989) *Transhomosexuality,* GENDYS International Gender Dysphoria Conference, Manchester England. *Ed* Purnell. A., British Library catalogue reference 4096.401960 DSC

Confusion exists between sexual preference and gender identity. The choice of a sexual or emotional partner is independent of matters of gender.

Homosexuality in men or women (lesbianism) is where one's 'sexual orientation' is towards persons of the same sex. It has very little to do with 'gender dysphoria' in the sense that most homosexuals and lesbians are quite satisfied with their sex and 'gender' (masculine or feminine) and their bodies as men or women.

Gender refers to culturally defined states of masculinity and femininity. It is not directly related to sex or to sexuality. It is a sense of a person being a boy or girl a man or a woman, and is about an individual's masculine or feminine behaviour and attitudes. Gender is behavioural and socio-psychological i.e. masculine or feminine. Gender is about identity, a sense of self, and about how others perceive us in the context of our society and behaviour.

Gender Identity is an individual's sense of being masculine or feminine and their gender role; it is a sense of being of one gender or another.

Gender Role is the public expression of gender identity.

Gender Behaviour is culturally prescribed and is polarised as masculine or feminine, with boundaries as defined by the society in which an individual lives. One is generally expected to conform to some extent to defined norms. What is *'expected'* in *'gender appropriate'* behaviour is linked to sex by society, to mating (sex) and to reproduction. In fact it is partly to do with the individual's sense of self and other's sense of that individual.

In popular and some professional thinking, sex and gender are used interchangeably. This muddled use of words conspires towards the lack of understanding in our heterocentric patriarchal society.

Gender stereotyping from a feminist perspective is a product of the patriarchal society in which we live, as indeed is feminism itself. However a sense of a gendered identity is inherent in most people. Whilst there are many who challenge gender stereotyping and the inadequacy of traditional gender roles, there are some who we term gender dysphoric. (Dysphoria is the opposite of euphoria). They are so oppressed by their own sense of incongruent gender identity, that they do not respond to any treatment to reverse that fundamental sense of self.*

(* Alice Purnell "Transsexualism, Transgenderism, and Gender Dysphoria" 1990)

Gender Dysphoria (Dissatisfaction) refers to a condition where there is a profound sense of unease or discomfort about one's gender (masculinity or femininity), which is in opposition to one's physical sex.

The Benjamin Syndrome.
According to the Harry Benjamin International Gender Dysphoria Association, *"the term gender dysphoria herein refers to that psychological state whereby a person demonstrates dissatisfaction with their sex of birth and the sex role, as socially defined, which applies to that sex, and who requests hormonal and surgical sex reassignment."*

13

"Gender dysphoria does not refer to cases of infant sex re-assignment or re-announcement. Gender dysphoria therefore, is the primary working diagnosis applied to any and all the persons requesting surgical and hormonal sex reassignment."

There are many ways in which the terminology used to describe the so called "sex-change" - transsexual, gender dysphoric, transgenderist, a sufferer of gender identity conflict - which reinforce confusion in people's minds. This confusion arises from differing ideas and convictions about what the words mean. It is how they actually describe the person, or the symptoms that person suffers from or experiences, when they are faced with having a core identity which is in conflict with their anatomy that adds to the problem.

We should note that even some very young children experience these symptoms. In **Primary Transsexual children** these experiences are usually pre-sexual, or at least pre-puberty. In these cases the gender identity is not confused. It is an unshakeable conviction that the body is out of step with the brain sex or mind. This is what causes confusion in the sufferer, which is so often exacerbated by feelings of what 'should be' rather than what is the physical situation.

There is a move to describe these symptoms as the Benjamin Syndrome instead of using such words as 'sex' or 'gender', which seem confused in most people's vocabularies. Once a person has resolved this conflict it seems absurd to describe them as "a transsexual" for example, as though they were not a whole person but a symptom or a history.

Below, in Italics, I quote the diagnostic descriptions given to these syndromes:

Transsexualism refers to a situation where *"a persistent discomfort and sense of inappropriateness about one's assigned sex in a person who has reached puberty."* (DSM3 302.50, 1991)

It refers to a condition where a person has such a strong gender dysphoria and conviction that they belong to the other gender than that of their sex at birth, that they seek to live and as far as possible adapt their life and their body, using all means available to be congruent.

Gender Identity Disorder (GID) of Adolescence or Adulthood, Non Transsexual Type (DSM3, 302.85)

"Cross dressing is not for the purpose of sexual excitement, it differs from transsexualism in that there is no persistent preoccupation with getting rid of the primary and secondary sex characteristics and acquiring those of the other sex."

14

Gender Identity Disorder of Childhood (DSM 3, 302.60, 1991)

"Is an intense and persistent distress in a child about his or her assigned sex and a desire to be, or insistence that he or she is, of the other sex."

Transsexual (TS) refers to a person who suffers from acute gender dysphoria. This refers to a condition not a person and is offensive and misleading, since it has much more to do with identity than with sex or sexuality.

It is inappropriate to describe a person as "a transsexual" who has resolved their condition of gender dysphoria and who now is physically and socially as far as possible able to function as a person of their perceived gender identity. We do not call a person who has had an appendix removed "an appendicectomy."

Transsexualism is a profound form of gender dysphoria, and persons thus affected have the conviction of being 'trapped in the wrong body' and feel compelled to express themselves in the gender to which they feel they belong. The transsexual is a person who feels an overwhelming need to live and function in the gender role 'opposite' to that of his or her biological sex.

Transexed an adjective that refers to a person who is/or was/suffering from transsexualism.

MtF is male to female

FtM is female to male

Trannie a slang term to include all transpeople

Trans a shorthand for a TV, TS, TG persons often used in sociological discourse

Transgenderism originally was a term used to cover all Trans phenomena. It occurs where an individual chooses to live fully or part time as the other gender. Increasingly this has come to mean without recourse to gender reassignment surgery.

Transgendered (TG) refers to a person who feels him/herself to feel more comfortable being in 'the other' gender than that expected considering their anatomy.

Transvestism or Cross-dressing (TV)* is where a person, usually male in Western society, has a compulsion to dress in the clothes of the other sex. It consists of cross-dressing and to an extent role-playing, and may be gender motivated (expeditions into their often stereotypical concept of a woman's life), or sexually motivated (often connected with fetishism).

Other forms of cross-dressing might be in connection with humiliation (where the forcing into the 'weaker sex's' clothes is involved). Cross-dressing also occurs in connection with drag (homosexual), with theatre, or with early sexual experimentation or fancy dress.

(* *Transvestism: A Guide*, Beaumont Trust 1992 and further Editions - see *Transvestism and Cross Dressing*, Beaumont Trust 2004)

Transvestite refers to a person who cross-dresses (TV= a person who cross-dresses) Transvestism is cross-dressing, with a compulsion to adopt the clothes, appearance and to an extent stereotyped behaviour normally associated with the opposite sex. In this culture and time, most transvestites are men, although women also cross-dress, perhaps for different reasons.

It can be seen that there is a gender continuum, as there is with sex. In fact this is part of natural variation in humans. Each individual responds to his or her sexual and gender identity and sexual preference with different amounts of pragmatism or guilt.

The medical and psychiatric, psychological, health and social welfare professionals respond with varying appropriateness or ineffectiveness to this range of people. There is a range of personal prejudices and degrees of empathy. Society and the law do not clearly recognise this variety of people with their particular behaviours and difficulties, which reinforces their sense of isolation, inequality and guilt.

Whether gender dysphoria is a response to nature or nurture or both is open to debate, but modern research suggests that brain sex is a reality and that gender programming occurs in the sixth week of gestation. There is now a strong case for saying that the foundations of a sense as to belonging to one sex (or one gender) or another is first established *in utero* and is absolutely fundamental in brain development.

Developmental psychologists place more emphasis on the nurture aspects of gender reinforcements and programming. Whatever the aetiology of this group of clients, a number of difficulties have been experienced in counselling the group who are most challenged by their gender dysphoria.

Androgyne refers to a person who wishes to belong to both or neither genders.

Abbreviations used in this book and generally used:

TS   in this publication refers to a transexed person (preferred vocabulary to "a transsexual").

TV   A person who cross dresses

GIC   Gender Identity Clinic

SRS   Sex Reassignment Surgery

GRS   Gender Reassignment Surgery

SOC   Standards of Care

NHS   National Health Service

BAC   British Association of Counsellors

CX   Charing Cross Hospital G.I.C.

Gerbil Gender Recognition Bill

3. Discussion: Sex, Sexual Identity, Gender and Sexual Preference. How does this Dysphoria arise?

It would seem there is no single answer. There are arguments for nature and for nurture, just as there are in the case of homosexuality. Lesbians and homosexuals are happy with their sex, indeed love other members of it (no pun intended!). They only very rarely would feel or 'want to be' transsexual - they are quite happy to be men loving men. Lesbians are content being and loving women.

Sexual identity seems to be in-born, and sexual preference a matter of preference, not a reflection of a person's own masculinity or femininity. Both situations have little to do with choice and could be linked to a genetic propensity. Choice comes after that is recognised.

Transvestites are generally heterosexual men. They do not 'become' Transexed, the symptoms are different.

Cross-dressing does take place for some, but not all, Transexed people. However the 'cross-dressing' of the transexed person is actually perceived by them to be that they dress as they 'should' dress. To accord with bodily evidence, rather than to do so 'as themselves', is to be permanently cross-dressed prior to resolving the problem.

Their feelings about their identity, in the gender to which they feel they 'belong' suggest that they are doing the right thing, but guilt then kicks in.

Few transvestites are homosexual, though it seems some are bisexual. Because of guilt some TV's do try to 'justify' their transvestism with a transsexual explanation, which if surgery is undertaken could be an irreversible mistake. Transvestism may have an early erotic element, and overlaps with fetishism in that respect, but some transvestites do express a gender duality, or might have, in their dreams, wished to have been women.

Transvestism seems to be about clothes, or expeditions into the other gender, about being a woman who is really a man, rather than about a sense of femaleness. In dressing as a female some feel more potent as males, enjoying the contrast. Some like to be seen as men-in-frocks, or as our American cousins say, "the chick with a dick"; whilst others slip into another role as well as a dress, as a way of relaxing from the pressures of being a man.

Some feel they need to develop an alternative identity, their 'second self'. Bancroft (1989) has coined the name "Dual Role Transvestite", although there are some who live permanently as women, terming themselves as transgenderists.

There appears to be a spectrum of so-called "normal, heterosexual - and happy with it - men", who wouldn't see the point of dressing as a female. They would incidentally be appalled at the prospect of a gay relationship or encounter. This spectrum continues through to the non-effeminate gay men who certainly don't want to be 'women'. Beyond this there are feminine men who are not gay or transvestites. Most transvestites are heterosexual, some bisexual, and some asexual, and some are homosexual.

'Trans-sexual' is a poor term in that it implies 'sex change' and somehow that it is about sex, not gender, whilst in fact this behaviour would seem rather to be confirmation of gender as perceived in the core identity of an individual. Trans people might be heterosexual or homosexual or asexual pre- or post- operatively. Sexual preference for them is as varied as in the rest of the population.

4.   Incidence.

It appears that, in the past decades in Britain, there was a ratio of about four 'male to female' transexed people to one 'female to male'. In recent years at Charing Cross Hospital the numbers of FtM TS's has increased, tending to approach the numbers of MtF's.

This difference in presenting requesting surgery may be explained by the fact the surgery FtM is not as relatively successful as for the MtF people.

It might be considered that the incidence of transsexualism may be a hidden constant. (People do not brag about being 'TS') and that those who appear seeking surgery reflect the 'state of the art' surgically, and the expense, and the society in which they live.

In Poland and the USSR more FtM's appear for reassignment. A rough guide might place the incidence of transsexuality at anything from one hundredth to one tenth that of transvestism, whilst transvestism may occur in up to 1% of the male population, with many people who cross-dress from time to time for fun.

5.   Cross Gender Manifestations - the Gender Spectrum.

All boys and girls and men and women probably wonder, from time to time, what it might be like to be the other sex. Many women feel it would be nice to be respected and taken seriously in the same way men usually are. Not being patronised would be great. Equally many men would like to feel pampered; to be allowed to cry, to wear attractive fabrics. Most children play dress-up games when they are small, but their peer groups put a stop to that as the gender divide becomes more apparent at school.

Thankfully the strict Victorian gender divide is being eroded, with women's rights, sexual freedom, equality laws, fashion challenges, new-men, women in responsible jobs, mixed sex-schools, paternity rights, male midwives, women in the Forces and so on. There is supposed to be gender equality in the Western World. But you still do not get men in skirts, unless they are brave or exhibitionists, pop stars or entertainers. It seems that women now have more gender freedom than men. Society still divides us all in terms of identity on all legally significant documentation.

19

Female transvestism in Western Society is hard to identify since dress codes for women allow for greater freedom; most women enthusiastically make incursions into the male fashion domain. They usually look better in a shirt than a man does in a skirt.

Most male transvestites are heterosexual, even often are macho men, in traditionally 'male jobs', especially, it would seem, engineering, in the UK. Years ago in Kent in the Beaumont Society there was a group of 'Steam Trannies', steam enthusiast-transvestites. That is a specialised subculture! These TV's who played with trains felt this combination of hobbies and interests was the ultimate for them.

There do seem to be local concentrations of TV's or TS's with jokes like "it might be something in the water" - to explain this. But the impression one gains by experience and researching the literature of anthropology, sociology, psychology, psychiatry and history, is that TV's and TS's have existed and occurred in all societies and cultures in the past as well as at the present.

Relatively few self-diagnosed TS's are "Primary" or easily identified - that is to say acutely Transexed. This is not to say that Secondary, or "Late-onset" Transsexuals are not genuine. Many MtF TS's try to suppress or hide their transsexualism by a flight into hyper-masculinity. The US Armed Services psychiatrists have found an unexpectedly high incidence of transsexualism in Vietnam front line veterans who sought psychological help after the Viet Nam war.

We hear a lot about the cliché of "a woman trapped in the body of a man", about the tomboy who hated her periods and fancied other girls. A person who struggles with their gender dysphoria may begin to understand what a cognitive leap it is for her or him, and so also for others, to realise that the packaging "should reflect the contents". This means that the body, or at least the acceptable gender in social terms, only feels really comfortable if **'self'** and others see the same thing, and interact accordingly.

There is a lot of pain and guilt attached to being 'different'. The Cult of Normality is dangerous; it sustains bigots, witch-hunters and bullies. Normality is seen as 'good', whilst abnormality is seen as 'bad'. It is seen as 'perverse', "against God and Nature".

To be abnormal in an ordered paternalistic state, is to be a lesser being'. A person has to be him/herself. Gender Dysphoria is not a mental illness. To be 'normal' is, many would say, to be average or ordinary, it does not say you are good or bad. A person has to be him/herself.

Gender Dysphoria is not a mental illness. It is 'normal' anyway to be part of nature, which encourages diversity!

6. A Question of Identity.

I repeat the term "Trans-sexual" is not really a good one, in the sense that the indications for this 'change' are more usually about gender than about sex. In another sense it works, because it is the physical sex, which needs to align with the gender identity for the person to feel complete.

Some Transexed people opt not to have surgery; some are advised not to do so for medical, social and other practical reasons. Some do have surgery; and others become obsessed about having more and more done surgically to their bodies.

The main issue for the Transexed person seems to be to establish an identity revealing an inner person, who can be socially accepted, or otherwise. Someone, who dresses as a female, was born one, looks and sounds like one, can not easily say to the world "I am a man" but in fact this may be true in terms of core identity. She can not penetrate a woman with her penis, and can not stand to urinate, but those things in themselves do not make a man a man or a woman a man. It is rather to do with self-image.

In a world where sex-role-stereotyping is obvious and dress codes for males and females always show differences, there have always been men and women who felt themselves not to be as their body dictated, who have expressed this in the way they have to decided to live their lives.

In so-called primitive or archaic societies such Transexed people were regarded as 'she-men' and often became Shamans. After exposure to Western Culture and values, they were often seen as 'unnatural women' and were regarded as witches.

There is a strange magic in belonging in both sexual camps, like the quantum leap from the natural to the supernatural - living between night and day, dark and light, life and afterlife. A blend point exists. To stand astride both genders can mean you are torn asunder, if both go in opposing directions. To encompass both, or choose one, in which you feel content and are comfortable, is probably preferable these days.

History and anthropology have shown us so many examples of transgendered people of one sort or another. There are even a few saints in the Christian faith and Gods in the Hindu belief.

7. How Sexual Identification is Established.

There are seven criteria for establishing Sexual Identification.

(After J.Money 1963 - See Sexual Identification in "Definitions")

The identity as a person of a particular sex or gender is not based on one variable alone, but is a composite of a number of variables.

In those suffering from transsexualism there is generally no apparent abnormality in five of these factors. They are: Chromosomal sex (normal male and normal female), gonadal sex (ovaries or testes), hormonal function, internal genital morphology and external genital morphology

What seems to be problematic is the Assigned sex (at birth) and Psychosexual differentiation. **I suggest that Brain Sex is a further variable factor to include.**

The term Gender Differentiation is shorthand used by later authors for the complex sequence of developmental factors proposed by Prof. Money. These operate at various times through life, especially in childhood and at puberty.

Among these will be an element from the social environment of the child - nurture as opposed to nature. It is the severe disturbance in this seventh stage, particularly in the sphere of gender identity, that is the concern of this book. While theories abound about causation, there is no proof of specific biological abnormalities in the hormonal or chromosomal make-up of most Transexed people. There may well be a genetic variable, which has yet to be identified. It is gender identity that seems to be the critical factor in evolution of and the need for appropriate care of the transgendered person.

Prof. Money's failed experiment in treating a boy infant, as a girl, who had by accident lost his penis, seems to suggest that it shows how strong the nature factor is against the nurture element.

It seems there is an inborn sense of personal gender.

(Prof. John Money had hoped this child would be able to lead a normal life having had 'female' genitals constructed, with hormones, and a life as a girl (from 1966). Sadly this ended in (Bruce/Brenda Reimer) eventually shooting himself (in May 2004 aged 38), after having tried to live as a man without a penis, in spite of his 'girlhood').

8. So What Makes a Person, is it Nature or is it Nurture?

I quote Chambers English Dictionary: *"Person - a character represented, a capacity in which one is acting, a living soul or a conscious being: a personality: a human being, Bodily form, human figure: Bodily presence or action. regarded as having rights and duties under law etc."* A person has identity as an individual and a sense of self. Each person has an unique history. Even identical twins have difference, although they may look the same. Parents know that it is how their twins behave which most demonstrates their individuality. Awareness, sentience (mind), consciousness and thought are each exclusively our own.

Identical twins may be born at the same time, look the same, have similar chromosomes, be treated the same, but they still are individual in thought, feelings and history. Nature gives us our body, nervous system etc. and rather like a computer we receive information on our hard-drives. Our Programme is partly dependent on what is loaded into our hard-drive by nature and nurture.

What comes out (how we behave), depends on what the machine can do, its memory and capacity, and it depends on what it is told to do by the programmer. Equally our sense of Gender depends on both Nature (the stronger of these factors) and on Nurture.

It is not our chromosomes which dictate what and who we are. It is a composite of many factors, not least our individual genes.

9. Aetiology ... The origins of gender dysphoria.

The formation of gender identity - one's essential maleness or femaleness - is probably the most important development in each person's life. This was thought to be absolute and irreversible from the first fertilised egg cell at conception, designated by XX or XY chromosomes.

Work by researchers into foetal development and others suggests that males and females are very similar in prenatal development and the foetal brain is sexually undifferentiated as either male or female. It must be 'instructed' as to its 'proper sexual role' (in the case of rats).

In the past, we have maximised sexual differences rather than similarities.

"The difference between male and female is not so much either/or but one of thresholds" (Prof. John Money).

Sexual similarity is most pronounced in the first six weeks after conception. The genitalia of both sexes are identical and have the capacity to differentiate in either direction at this stage.

There are four major sex differentiation 'forks' in the progress between conception and birth, any one of which can produce an ambiguous sexual differentiation. The first is the sex chromosomes themselves, which may besides the usual XX or XY configuration, have the configuration of X0, XXX, XXY, XYY, XXXY, X/XY, X/XX, XY/XYY and so on.

It was thought that the expected XY 'male' or XX 'female' chromosomes dictated your sex and gender. In general, these chromosome anomalies produce quite noticeable physical effects from birth, or at puberty. There may even be mosaics, where a person has mixed chromosomes. It is probable these chromosome anomalies are not as rare as originally postulated.

The importance of the Y chromosome from our point of view, lies in one small gene, the SRY gene, which, for a few hours in the first days of life, expresses a protein, the Testes Determining Factor (TDF). This small, singular event sets the course of people's whole lives, as Cookson points out, in *The Gene Hunters,* whether or not they will be accepted as priests in the Catholic Church, for instance.

Whatever the differences between women and men, they are not based in genetic inheritance; for the majority of genes are as identical as they are between any two individuals.

At six weeks, if TDF is produced, development is directed along a male path, and the two undifferentiated gonads normally develop into testes. These produce hormones which, from then on, act on receptors to foster male development and suppress female development. Otherwise, at twelve weeks, they become ovaries, and development

24

proceeds in a female direction. At about this time, the external genitals are formed. If there is a failure in this complex process, confusion may occur.

Money suggests all humans are undifferentiated at the onset and nature's first preference is to differentiate a female. That's the 'Eve principle'. The masculinising hormone (Androgen) must be added to incite a male. That's the 'Adam principle'. When development depends on the addition of something it is easier to make a mistake. Nature does, in fact, make more mistakes in differentiating the male. Where Nature 'fails' or partly fails in the application of the Adam principle, then the sexual development reverts back to the Eve principle.

This all helps to account for the many varieties of intermediate physical sex. This idea has been extended to suggest that there may be a hormonal stimulus to the foetal brain to develop a 'male' or 'female' and superimposing (in a 'normal' function usually) to accord or discord with the development of the anatomy of the baby.

Prof. Money said *" ... gender identity differentiation of the brain after birth is a process that resembles the differentiation of the internal sex organs, in that neither the male nor the female system is totally or completely obliterated, but one becomes dominant over the other ... "* This is an elegant Nature rationale for why and how 'mistakes' - or variations (put more precisely), can occur. Thus pathogenic, social and psychological factors in child rearing combine nature and nurture.

Other researchers suggest transsexualism is due to a subtle organic dysfunction, possibly related to prenatal endocrine influences on the developing thalamus. Levine, in 1971, combined the two theories into an hypothesis involving the sequential actions of chromosomes, hormones and learning mechanisms at critical stages in development.

This author feels, as a feminist, a reluctance to accept the idea of a male brain versus a female one, but increasingly researchers are demonstrating this concept as a viable hypothesis. Yet such researchers have always been in disarray. For every argument there has been a counter-argument. As an example, at one time, statistics suggested that girls performed better in junior school, then reached a plateau in teenage. Boys, it was thought, made a late start, but then passed the girls.

Now it is apparent that girls are not only maintaining their lead, but also extending it. Thus changing attitudes to women is changing their psychology, in not underachieving through peer-pressure. There may also, though, be changes in the employment environment, which benefit girls, particularly in a requirement for communication skills.

Certainly a boy brought up as a girl, may be happy to 'be one', but may not. Studies on identical twins show the nurture theory on its own is not an exclusive answer. To suggest a biological basis is not to deny the effect of social learning - after all, being human has a biological basis.

A better piece of evidence of the 'Nature' idea seemed to be a higher than expected presence of the 'Y' antigen in the skin of 'male' TS's (this is normally found in women). However, this hypothesis is not now thought to be supported.

Professor Louis Gooren, the world's only Professor of Transsexuality, who worked at the Free University Hospital, Amsterdam until 2003, said at the 1994 GENDYS Conference at Manchester University, *"We are still far away from understanding how maleness and femaleness works, let alone understanding the aetiology of gender identity conflict."* He talked, among other things, of the work done in the Netherlands on the brains of transsexuals post mortem, where an area known as the interstitial nuclei of the hypothalamus may show a biological difference, those brains of the MtF post mortem resembling women's brains rather than a man's. However there were only six brains to investigate, so the sample is too small to provide empirical, utterly convincing evidence of a clear biological rationale for transsexualism.

What is most probable is that the aetiology is a mixture of biological and environmental factors.

On the other hand, the very fact that transsexualism has found expression in so many different ways in so many cultures throughout history indicates that the 'Nurture' model is not sufficient by itself. Whatever the virtues and faults of our culture, it cannot be changed overnight, but we all have a duty to ensure that all its members can grow and prosper in freedom, while respecting the freedom of others and expecting it from them.

What is certain is that a great deal more research is needed. The idea of a male mind trapped in a female body, or vice versa, although trite, is in all probability a fact.

This results in the dreadful dilemma of gender dysphoria. It really is a question of identity - not 'just' sexual identity.

26

There is a sense that each of us is both male and female, but that naturally society (and most of us) prefers that we clarify this issue by how we live our lives and who we are. Of course parents in particular find it a terrible affront if their boy or girl, who is 'obviously' a boy or girl 'decides' to be a woman or man against the evidence of their external genitalia.

The human mind is perhaps nature's most complex system; the brain is little understood. What is surprising is that anybody is 'normal'. It is rather a pity that normal equates with 'good' philosophically, and it might be more fair in a moral and a Newtonian sense to regard these 'abnormalities' as variations - without the inbuilt 'criticism' of linguistic 'pseudo-moralistic sloppiness' (and that's a mouthful for a start!).

However gender dysphoria occurs, the fact is that it exists, and needs to be addressed. Those who refer to gender reassignment as an "elective process", close their minds to the very real distress that many people endure. Those who see it as a matter of choice ignore the fact that none of us chooses our biology *or* our childhood. Our options are thereby constrained and our choices are concerned with preparing for a better future.

Those who advocate the Nurture principle suggest mechanisms, such as being spurned by a mother wanting an opposite sex child. Some even postulate having been consciously brought up as a member of the opposite sex.

Gender-role is established in the first four years of childhood and the parental, especially maternal, role in helping an infant establish this is obviously important.

Unfortunately the work of Freud, and others, though making an important contribution towards understanding some behaviours, has enabled people to find trite answers to complex questions, using some of his very outdated psychological models to try to explain 'deviations' from the norm.

With deviation comes the stigma of the 'deviant', or the 'pervert', from which homosexuals have suffered in much the same way as the Transexed person.

In searching for a nurture model to explain how transgendered feelings evolve, the same rather simplistic possible background models and rationales were sought by researchers to explain these conditions.

Examples were suggested such as the presence of a dominant mother as a role model for a baby boy. Alternately an absent or violent father (invoking rejection of the male role model), an over-protective mother, or the positive reinforcement of anti-male messages from a mother who has rejected her father or husband, and his sex, and as a consequence, transfers them to the child.

Indeed these may influence individual children, as psychological keys, but the potential has to be there. Children expected to show all of these factors do not inevitably 'become Transexed' - in fact very few do - and in families, siblings, even in identical twins, different responses to the same home environment are clearly seen.

It seems obvious that it is difficult to be a parent, but to blame parents would be a mistake. Blame is not an issue in matters like this. If a child becomes a great musician parents can take pride, but much of this ability will have come from the individual and what action he, or she, undertook.

10. A Cure? and Why "Change Sex"?

Although researchers have tried hypnosis, hormones, aversion therapy, electroconvulsive therapy, psychotherapy, psychoanalysis, primal therapy etc., **there is no evidence of a 'cure'.** You can not 'cure' homosexuality either.

These variations of the usual are a part of the variety of human life, and although adjustments can be made, self-control and other controls can be applied. In some cases, the only reasonable approach is to change lifestyle, and body form, if feasible, and 'change sex'.

Sex itself can not be fully changed by all the medical criteria. Social sex role can be. Surgery can help many to gain a body-mind accord. Social changeover can be enough for many people. This change is achieved as a sex confirmation or affirmation rather than just a modification.

Dr. Virginia Prince (of the USA) and others have suggested that *"intelligence and social effectiveness increase dramatically, once a person has confirmed his or her sex."* Post changeover and particularly post surgery - if it has a good outcome, the trans person has a major psychological distraction relieved and, for many, their lives are dramatically transformed. Of course some mistakes are made.

The greatest mistake is to imagine it is 'easier' being a woman or 'better' being a man. For some women life is 'easy' - for some men life is 'better'. Life itself and all it challenges us with, will continue to depress and to delight each and all of us. It is how we deal with these challenges that is important and significant.

Psychiatrists tend towards the Nurture model, whilst biologists might lean towards genetics as to what creates a person. Obviously it is a combination, but which is the major factor?

Being seems to come from nature, whilst **feelings** derive to some extent from nurture, with elements of nature at a more primal level.

How does a cat know it is a male or a female, or a cat for that matter? It does know when it needs food or milk. The urge to reproduce is certainly programmed by the hormones, which affect the brain (and by the proteins resulting from our DNA and the so-called "selfish genes").

Desmond Morris with his "Naked Ape" compared human behaviour to that of our cousins the apes, providing further food for thought. Which feelings come from thought, experience and learning and which from chemistry (hormones) from our ancestors in the gene pool?

11.   Natural Variations.

It strikes me that few things in life are clear-cut, save that we are mortal. Sex and sexuality and gender each are a continuum and each is independent, although generally of course one is either male or female, masculine or feminine, heterosexual or homosexual. But what of the hermaphrodite and intersexed people, of the gender neutral, of the bisexual and the asexual person? These are all **natural** variations.

There was a television programme some time ago by a gay man investigating gay animals. It seems that of course they do exist. The amygdala in the brain of a gay ram is more like that of a ewe than his male hetero-rams. He cannot but be other than he is, in that he is attracted to males even in the presence of ewes in oestrous. Sexuality seems to be driven by the wiring in a part of the brain.

In fact a physical anatomical gender difference is seen in the stria terminalis of the human brain, if Dutch research by Prof. Swaab is valid.

A biological reason for gender or sexual behaviours gets people off the 'guilty' hook of having somehow chosen to challenge what is termed 'normality'

Prof. Petra De Sutter* shows that there is robust scientific data, which does not support a mental illness hypothesis as a rationale for gender dysphoria.

* Sutter. P., (2004) *Using Science And Medicine To Serve Gender Dysphoric And Transsexual People,* Press for Change: The 6th International Congress on Sex and Gender Diversity: Manchester. There is an abstract on the GIRES website *http://www.gires.org.uk/*

12. Stereotypes.

The Christian idea of 'everything in its proper place' as a pre-Renaissance concept - there being God, angels, saints, men, women, children, beasts and so on - has provided a comfortable fixed structure, but has tended to restrict humans from developing their individual potential strengths.

It has also created a structured rigid world where all is seen as in its place and without any liberty to exist beyond a black or white, male or female, essence or position.

Sadly Christianity, the religion of love, as it is preached or even sometimes practised, often leaves the Transexed person in a no-man's-land, to carry the guilty inheritance of the Old Testament, without the liberation of loving acceptance. The traditional, patriarchal Judeo-Christian and Islamic views of structure and position, male or female, has all too often only reinforced the sense of isolation and guilt experienced by those who are different.

This rigidity tends to somehow dehumanise the societies in which we live. Christianity could be accused of failing these people, as could Western Society, since both Church and State find it difficult to accept that within this so-structured society are individuals with particular problems, which give rise to feelings of challenging order. These challenges are not based on moral actuality, but upon social and practical issues.

With Church, State, family and physical body all feeling, or apparently seeming to be 'against' the Transexed person, it is not surprising that she/he often feels bereft of anywhere to turn.

The real truth about the public perception of this problem is probably more like the emotion expressed in *Gone with the Wind:* "Frankly my dear I don't give a damn".

Most people are not concerned about, or are ignorant of, the Transexed and her/his plight. But some of course are actively intolerant. The good news is that, as we move into this Millennium, intolerance is not politically correct, so the bigot is becoming a public target.

Clearly to be out of accord with your body is most painful - as we know with age, or when we remember what it was like when we were children. To be in accord with your body is wonderful, better still to be in accord in body, mind and spirit; we get back to identity.

The dysphoria that some feel is so acute that they simply can not go on living as they are. Once resolved, all that energy can go towards living a quality life.

It is a genuine handicap to be gender dysphoric. To overcome it is a triumph. As the deaf can learn to speak, have hearing aids, lip-read, sign and learn to communicate with and blend with society; the gender dysphoric person has degrees of dysphoria, degrees of ability, of gifts in dealing with the problems, degrees of success or failure at self, and then public, acceptance. She or he has quite as much right as the deaf person to be an accepted, healthy, happy full member of society.

Gender Dysphoria resolved, such a person can move logically to Gender Euphoria. Then they have to learn how to live as well adjusted people, having not so much discovered as released themselves. However, some have a chip on the shoulder to remove!

It seems strange that anyone should become "a transsexual", as it is such a tortured path, with much psychological pain, and at such a high price - sometimes possibly too high. But that might imply there is such a choice in the first place. The choice is really how to live in harmony with self and others, the dysphoria is not 'willed away'.

A transvestite may resolve his situation by living as a man with expeditions into 'womanhood' as he, often stereotypically, sees it - by dressing up and 'being a woman' in private or public.

A transgendered person may live 'full-time' as a woman (or man) without feeling the need for surgery. A Transexed person may, because of practical reasons like age, family, health risks, build, finances, long waiting lists and for other reasons, just give up and try to cope. Some opt for trying to short cut this, by turning to private clinics and surgeons that may, or may not, abide by proper Standards of Care. This means, in some cases, inappropriate surgery may be performed, or appropriate

31

surgery may be performed before the patient is ready or properly assessed.

Gender Identity Clinics are attended by larger numbers of people hoping for help than they can accommodate. Such 'help' as the state affords, can, it seems at present, only be minimal. There are some individuals who 'give all the right answers' and receive surgical 'help', perhaps without proper self-assessment, counselling, or thorough proper assessment by a psychiatrist with the support of qualified and experienced counselling.

Surely it is important that the right person receives the appropriate treatment as an individual, with particular individual circumstances, so that an appropriate lifestyle can be reached, and lived without the overlay of stereotypes. Trans people are as diverse as any group; each has different strengths and weaknesses, vulnerabilities and degrees of confidence, gifts and disadvantages.

There is no such thing as a "typical Transsexual person". They should not attempt to be stereotypical women or men, but surely might be permitted to be themselves, with all the resources and interests they have. Most women and men have moved beyond the stereotypes. Male to female transexed people are often criticised for having a very stereotyped view of womanhood and trying too hard to be feminine and not hard enough to be female.

13. Boys will be Boys.

Over the last several millennia warring states felt the need for clarity, dipolarity; so men went to war and women bore children and stayed home and wept. If you remember your mythology Achilles' mother tried to spare him death in battles by disguising him, this great Greek hero, as a girl when he was a child. But when he was offered a spear or a distaff, the twit chose a spear, revealing his maleness that way. So he eventually found himself in Troy where he finally met his fate thanks to his Achilles heel. But remember any half-decent Amazon would have done the same thing.

Even Heracles after his great Labours and adventures went to live in a cave with the witch Omphale, where he dressed as a woman and spent his time spinning, bewitched by this woman. This shows the power of women and the weakness of men I suppose, but after his encounter with the Gorgon who can blame him?

Despite the Greek Republic being described as a democracy and idealised, it was an androcracy (only men voted). Interestingly the Greeks, with their Gods and Goddesses, were not homophobic, that came with Judeo-Christianity and an all-male-God. It is sad that we have made God in the image of a man, though Christ did turn His back on male power with His ideas of love one another.

14. Humans are Not Particularly Sexually Dimorphic.

Back to biology - in many species males and females are markedly dimorphic - stag or doe, peacock or peahen. Especially among the birds there are display differences which become exaggerated so that females can choose a mate. Some male spiders are so tiny as to seem a different species to the females, who eat them anyway after mating! These differences have evolved in such a way that the successful creature develops display colours, feathers, antlers, size differences, rituals, behaviours and so on.

Humans are actually less sexually dimorphic than most other mammals. There seems to be less anatomic difference between human males and females, but more social differences than one might expect. Male nipples and the clitoris seem to be vestiges, but they reveal a little of the fact that there is a potential in any embryo towards either male or female sexual embryonic development from the 'female' phenotype. During the growth of a foetus there are vestiges of our history as creatures in evolutionary terms and of the individual in sexual terms.

In our nearest relatives in the animal world, the chimps, sexual dimorphism is more apparent than in humans. Dominant males are very much bigger, and stronger, than the females, or their less dominant brothers and rivals. As social creatures, like ourselves, their genes are to an extent their destiny; most males behave one way and females another. Their society is stratified, with alpha males and alpha females, with issues of position and dominance in the group or tribe clearly defined and tested during childhood and adolescence, by play and by the status of their parents (especially the mother).

The way we perceive others and ourselves perceive us is to a great extent defined by our gender and its place in society. During the last two millennia of patriarchy various 'norms' and prohibitions have dictated the roles and reflecting this, the dress, of men and women.

But boys are expected to be boys; and girls to be girls, from day one of a child's life. Blue for a boy, pink for a girl is the norm. Research at the University of Sussex demonstrated that parents behave differently to baby girls and boys, reinforcing the passivity of the girl and the robustness of the baby boy.

It is hard for a mother to accept that her little girl has grown up to become a man, or is a dyke, often much harder, for example than if she is a drug addict, alcoholic or a criminal. Perhaps it is even harder for an only son of a Moslem to be accepted by his father as a woman.

15.   Women in a Man's World.

The MtF T person joins the 'wrong side' in a man's world and it would seem suffers more approbation than her FtM counterpart. Our society has only offered women the right to property and to the vote during the last century and there is still some way to go for real equality. Only during the last eighty years have Western women gained something like equality in matters of political power, ownership, position in the law, creativity or being taken seriously as sentient beings.

No longer are we 'owned' by men - by our father, then a husband, with the somewhat limited expectation of dependency and housework and children. Since the advent of the pill many women enjoy the same sexual freedom as men. At the same time better education, strong role models and challenges to male superiority, mean that women are moving towards something a little nearer equality. Though traditional 'female' jobs are still paid about 20% less per hour than male ones.

So I wonder why anyone with a brain might want to think of themselves as a woman when there are still such inequalities? But that is not really the point, I suggest that a person's gender identity is fixed before birth. Normally a girl has a female gender identity, and she is stuck with it.

It seems some people are born with the 'wrong' chromosomes (or more probably genes). It is not an 'XX or XY chromosome' which only defines sex. It is more complex than that, just as the genes themselves are complex, together with the proteins and the numerous copies of SRY among the genome affecting sex and probably gender. Sex is more complex than a Y chromosome probably being an incomplete X, and the Y always making a male of the foetus. Much further research needs to be done to clear up this situation, especially concerning the interaction of the genes.

16.   Variation is Natural.

If we think of the fertilised egg as a potential person, it is generally, but not always, possible to predict the sex of the embryo defined by the genes, visible to some extent in the pairs of chromosomes. These genes probably act as switches as the foetus develops, as do hormones produced by the foetus and in the maternal blood stream. Physical and neurological growth takes place, so that nine months later a reasonably healthy baby will hopefully be born, with its own body map developing in its brain. Gender Identity depends on all the 'right switches' operating at the right times, the right hormones, temperatures, timings… so many variables, not least the genetic makeup. The environment within the womb needs to be perfect - no stress, drugs, chemicals, cigarettes, hormones, the right acidity etc.

Then comes Nurture after the baby is born. We are all accidents or experiments of nature. To a lesser extent I think Nurture also has a role in reinforcing or releasing inherent traits.

Variation, including gender identity, is a natural consequence of the complexities of human development. Even by year two of a child's life he or she will probably know how he or she should behave, because of all the positive and negative reinforcement of his parents and his peer group. Usually the child will not need to challenge this.

I believe that a sense of gender identity is latent at birth. By the time we are adults we know well all the prohibitions about crossing gender divides, especially if a boy has been a sissy. There is denial about being feminine if you were born a boy, less so about being a tomboy if you were a girl.

There is a caution in all this. Hate of one's sex or gender is not the best reason to adopt the other. This is **reactive gender identity disorder,** rather than one which is a drive towards what is right, it is away from what was unpleasant. There are no guarantees that the other side of the fence will be any less uncomfortable. I have met clients who I would describe as autoandrophobic, hating maleness, because of some trauma in earlier life.

35

A sense of being is a stronger indicator of self, rather than a sense of not being. Both sets of feelings are equally powerful.

It is also dangerous to rationalise that you are living in the wrong gender if you prefer the clothes of the other, or as a guilty transvestite you feel released from guilt, if you describe yourself as a Transexed person. It is a big and almost irreversible step to officially and physically permanently cross the gender divide. Costs are high, so one needs to be certain. I do not just mean financial costs, but emotional costs to those we love and who love us.

Your genes are not always your destiny. These challenges to identity can mean that the search for, and a sense of, personal identity, of whatever gender; allows those with gender identity disorder to question, in a very healthy way, the whole ridiculous inequalities which still exist in our society. Gender is only one dimension on being a person.

In a sense what sort of man or woman or ungendered or polygendered person you are is an even more challenging question. A personal identity is vital to each of us. Many are not so challenged. Many T people would prefer to never have had to face these problems and the challenges of an unsympathetic society. However perhaps Society will soon be celebrating diversity in a rainbow world, where there is plenty of room for difference.

Frequently a person with gender identity disorder feels sure about his or her gender, but they also feel isolated, rejected, confused, betrayed, not good enough, guilty, even suicidal. Surely they should be enabled to feel liberated, freed, joyful by that recognition and experience. There is a high price to pay for freedom. Sadly partners may also be hurt and families disrupted.

17. Sex, Like Gender, is Not Dipolar.

Nobody is as the papers say "Born a man", thank God. Imagine the consequences of trying to give birth to a twelve-stone eighteen-year-old man? No, a baby is born. It might look like a boy or a girl, but many are in-between or unclear. That is based on what we see of their genitals and has incomplete authority over their identity.

So called "birth defects" are not rare. In a six week period as a Theatre Sister in a local children's hospital, I saw eleven such children, with Testicular Feminisation (XY Chromosomes, but no penis). There were many others with various problems ranging from hypospadias to genital ambiguity. The genitals do not always conclusively define a child's sex or gender for that matter. Parental shame hides the numbers of these unfortunate children.

Humans are complex, we may be born male or female, both, or in very rare cases neither, they may prove to become hetero-, homo-, bi-, or asexual in terms of sexual preference.

During the late 19th. and early 20th. century Freud developed his theories of psychoanalysis. These have a somewhat misogynist and pessimistic pervading view of humanity, driven largely by ego based, often dark, forces which could be manipulated by a psychoanalyst or psychiatrist, or by a paternalistic State. His followers adopted and adapted these theories to manipulate the masses by advertising and brainwashing. They used controls of 'normalcy' and made 'average', 'normal' and 'standard', as something to strive for and to control populations, even to sell ideas and goods to.

This replaced religious faith with its own mythologies and consumer driven values creating a standard consumer in a materialistic world in which economics became the driver. This Cartesian view of humanity fails to see the person. A person-centred, client-led, Humanistic and existential view of the individual allows for variation among individuals. This humanistic approach challenges Freudian psychology in that it recognises that there is much that is to be said for personal autonomy. There is also much that is innately good in people. Of course not all individuals are innately good or altruistic, nor are all people selfish or bad for that matter. Neither are we doomed to anarchy if we recognise the person.

After the second World War ideas about individuality, existentialism and freedom have allowed many people to look deeply into who they really are, in terms of sexuality, sex and gender, rather than live unchallengingly as who they 'should be'. People are coming out of all sorts of closets. As the closets empty to cries of "freedom, respect, equality" - Cabinet makers, lawyers and politicians shudder! The conventional, the insecure, the powerful and the bigot fall off their perches and feel frantic about the challenges to "family life, society and the world, as we know it".

It is a shame that ethical and religious matters have become embroiled in this debate, because belief is challenged by the existential. There is great fear of anarchy among the hierarchical. But there is no excuse for intolerance, save when the behaviour of one damages another (abusers, rapists, drug pushers, terrorists, paedophiles and murderers, do need to be stopped).

18.   Attitudes of Society.

Trans is an unglamorous condition. Public sympathy is almost non-existent. The media, the churches, people's own vulnerable sexualities faced with this problem, mean that a public view of the situation varies from amusement to embarrassment, to outright hostility. Understanding is not great, even in the medical world.

Samaritans report very large numbers of suicidal calls from transgenderists, mainly based on extreme guilt and self-disgust or isolation. Thus, it can be seen the GD person is in a particularly difficult position, which does deserve some sympathy and understanding. The family, spouse, employer, state, law and the transexed, will be looked at later. What can be said is that the disability of gender dysphoria has large repercussions on the family, and a great deal of sympathy for them also deserves to be offered.

The view of medicine and surgery in the UK, except in the few centres of excellence, seems to be behind those of many States of the USA and much of Europe. The laws of England and Wales, and of Scotland and the Irish Republic, were not altogether helpful, until 2004, with respect to marriage and to the birth certificate issues. Ireland is still unjust in treatment of its Transexed citizens.

The media can be seen as the traditional 'bad boys' in reinforcing a hostile, suspicious and unsympathetic public perception of the gender dysphoric person.

Just as the gay man was assumed to be a child molester, the gender dysphoric person was portrayed as a pervert, anti-society, against the fabric of the common good, evil at worst, crazy or, at best, good for a laugh.

In the post-war period until quite recently, Asians and black people could read in the tabloid press, or see on chat shows on television, the attitude, commonly portrayed and even adopted, "You wouldn't want one moving next door to you." What the media did to so called 'sex-changes' was on a par with their treatment of Princess Diana, they were sometimes hounded to death.

Now, however it is the bigot who is seen as the threat. Extremists, I am sorry to say, do not seem to be hounded but given media exposure. Some even make a good living by writing bigoted prose. It is, after all, a good 'debate', good for circulation, good for public titillation. The papers sell a story by being selective with the truth.

19.   Religious and Ethical Questions.

Religion is to do with belief. Ethics is the science of morals; it is that branch of philosophy, which is concerned with human character and conduct. The Christian churches have no official stance of the position of the Transexed and marriage, save that they generally hold that marriages are not valid, because "you can not marry two people of the same sex".

The Church is so often behind in knowledge of Science and common sense (e.g. How lepers were treated, how wise-women were burnt as witches, how Jews were exterminated, and these days objecting to Gene Therapy, and to Birth control (in an over populated world), and divorce when a third of marriages fail).

A man can not marry a trans-woman in church, but can get a blessing in some churches. Jewish, Moslem, Anglican and Catholic Clerics are fearful of marrying two men or two women. In the USA. the Evangelical Churches have approved marriages involving transpeople. In Denmark blessings are openly given to Trans (or to gay) unions and in GB some churchmen will bless unions between a known TS and his/her partner.

In some countries marriages are possible, and the author knows some TS monks and nuns in EEC countries. The various churches, which tend to be conservative in these cases, seem to have a view on the TS and marriage which depends to some extent on the circumstances, and the individual churchman or woman. Generally any tendency to liberalisation and acceptance of the post-operative man or woman as a whole man or woman, is rather behind that of the law in many countries.

Perhaps now the law has altered; the Church of England at least may possibly follow suit. They do have women priests. However, they are still terrified of 'gay' marriages or Bishops.

The ethics of TS surgery is another problem for some TS's, and indeed for some surgeons. To those Christian denominations, which are very Old Testament orientated, the idea of 'mutilation' is considered relevant in case of the TS surgery. All people are to be loved by their God, or that deity would not be worthy of worship. Packaging has little to do with the contents. We can feel certain that a person who has been crippled is not seen as such by a compassionate Creator.

Quoting one of Isaiah Berlin's talks *"a romantic would say, 'To any question there is more than one answer'."* He quotes Bishop Butler on meaning, *"Everything is what it is and nothing else"* Rand goes on to say *"Liberty is liberty and nothing else."* So supposing we are created, we are created with variation, and each deserves a voice and respect from the rest, that is liberty. Let us aim at the fundamentalists here.

Liberation is very important, including of the self. Rational men and women have blemishes removed, lose weight, and alter their body image - is this harmful? One would think not. If healers are instruments of God, then to heal the tortured mind of an unhappy person, by helping reach him or her to find compatibility of body and self-image, this can only be good, so how could this be thought harmful?

Gender Dysphoria is classified as a disease. "Dis-ease" is to say out of ease with oneself in this case. We should surely learn to love ourselves. Should self-hate and disgust mutilate the mind? Other questions arise - if God is the Creator, has man the right to 'interfere' with this creation? So do we let people die or stay crippled or starve?

How can we justify the almost inevitable break-up of families, marriages, and the hurt to parents, spouse, and children? In deepest depression we may ask, "Why me?" There is a sense that God has turned His/Her back on those who suffer. The questioning of one's faith, one's God's 'unkindness' in allowing this injustice is so very common with anyone who suffers in some way. The thinking Transexed person asks so many of these rhetorical questions.

Fascinating speculations can evolve like "are Angels androgynous?" Indeed, are they transvestites, or are they hermaphrodites? Is 'God the Father' the only sense in which God exists? God the Mother is just as

40

valid for some. Surely the Soul is without sex or gender, as is God. Identity transcends sex and gender.

In Genesis we are told "God saw that it was good" - i.e. all creation was good. Variants exist in all of nature. Hermaphrodites, or change of sex, are an integral part of some creature's life cycles and occur quite naturally in nature. Many creatures reproduce parthenogenetically (without mating - they clone themselves). A greater view might best be taken. Moralising does not help. In the Hindu religion manifestations of the Gods are male and female or both, and Eastern faiths do tend to allow a greater acceptance of 'things as they are'. The orthodox Jew, and the Islamic Fundamentalist, would have considerable difficulty in reconciling their religion and their predicament if Transexed.

This author's view is that religion was made for man and woman, not that people were made for religion. We create God in our own image, so the paternalists gave us the old man with a beard, the man on the cross and the women weeping below. We surely have a loving God, who is also compassionate and pragmatic. Learning from this, a compassionate view should extend to all of us, as well as to others. All effort should be made to try not to hurt others, or punish minorities for being different. What is between our ears is more important than what is between our legs, and what we do with dysphoria is to a large extent a matter of personal conscience and circumstance.

A good Biblical view is *"Judge not that you be not judged,"* and Christ's own instruction to *"Love one another"* can not be equalled let alone bettered.

It is unethical to deny people equal rights and respect, before each other, the Law or God.

20.   Those who Oppose Equality for "T people".

We still have sad strange creatures purporting to speak for Christianity in the Evangelical Alliance … They are never consistent. They select texts from the Old Testament and forget the loving text of the New. Do they think we should leave a hair lip as it is, or not strive to improve quality of life for our people?

As Christians can they assume that their God actually wishes us to keep slaves and punish them in particular ways as described in the

'Good Book'? Have they forgotten the Sermon on the Mount and the Prayer of St. Francis?

In fact the Bible suggests we should stone to death those guilty of adultery, how to keep slaves, to have polygamous marriages, to pluck our eyes out - if through them there is a possibility of sin and so on. Do these zealots promote these ideas? I think not. It amazes me that fellow Christians judge others by Old Testament standards, when for example they would not cut off the hand of a thief, or pluck out their offending eye?

These misguided people seem ignorant of intersexed people, of feelings of identity, which they have never been exposed to. They even appear to be unaware of the fact that diversity is an important part of nature. If a Creator made us She/He did so with love accepting each of us as we are.

As a counselling psychologist I meet clients who have gone, or are going through hell, because of the negative attitude they share with some vocal members of our society. These vocal individuals speak as if to represent society, indeed all people, in belittling or somehow disbelieving that the mind is stronger than the body.

We each have an identity, a personality. Most religions would say a soul.

The result of our thoughts, feelings, actions and interactions shows who we are. This soul, we are told by the religious, is stronger than the body and has an eternal life after death. The argument to leave things "as God made them" simply does not stand up to genuine Christian values.

If mind is incongruent with the body, an internal war takes place, resulting in a range of symptoms, which are painful and harmful to the sufferer.

If that person is also assailed by the so-called upholders of morality and the thought-police mentality of some of these bigots this hardly helps.

Many of my clients feel confused and suffer great guilt trips about being different, having been bashed by many a Bible, an unsympathetic world, or by simply realising how upset their parent feels about their son or daughter's gender affirmation.

The media will always give room to Thought-Luddites. Even some misguided professionals, who should know better, choose to have their say without any understanding of the problem.

Surely the triumph of Reality over Fantasy is to recognise that the world is inhabited by diverse people, not just ordinary so called 'normal' men or women. In the same way that there is a spectrum of races, colours, creeds, beliefs, abilities, disabilities, sizes, intelligences, education and skills, our Society must recognise this and give respect to each individual.

We know there are lies, damn lies and statistics. It is undeniable that Statistics can show trends.

If we think about the dominant role of Patriarchy based on Normality, statistically it is interesting. There are about sixty million U.K. Subjects. Of these about a third are elderly, a third are under 18 years old, 51% are female, at least 5% are gay, 10% are immigrants, 2% collectively are blind, or deaf, diabetic, with others registered disabled. This leaves only about sixteen million men who in the UK are in none of these minority groups. The 'real men' who run everything are in fact a minority, perhaps that is why they cling on to power so arduously, fearful of a take-over in the 'moral high ground' in the State, Church, Stock Exchange, Forces and so on.

Even after hostile attitudes change and the law changes, there will still be frightened children, lonely confused T adults and others, who will need some understanding and help from caring professionals. Hopefully one day we might have a Society, which is genuinely not fearful of difference.

21.   Guilt Trips.

To be different means generally to be made to feel not as good, guilty, ashamed. The playground bully starts this abuse, which leads to loneliness and fear. So fearful are some that they take their own life or drown their sorrows with alcohol.

The weapons of the bigot are the same as those of the abuser, using fear, guilt, and power to control the victim. Why, one wonders, do some people react so negatively to those they perceive as different? Lepers still exist in our land, minorities who are not accepted are easy targets for the bigots, media, and unenlightened. Stereotyping is a good way to

43

dehumanise ... the immigrants, blacks, Moslems, Jews, cripples, asylum-seekers, gays and Trannies ...

Perhaps it becomes harder to be a bigot when you see a real person whose aspirations to be loved, respected, accepted are as reasonable as your own.

22. Transgendered Behaviour in History and Biography.

Historical and biographical incidence of transgender behaviours is very numerous. Even a cursory glance at anthropology and mythology shows examples of Transgenderism. In Greek mythology the son of Hermes and Aphrodite was transformed into a being both male and female - Hermaphroditus.

Heracles was dressed as a woman by the witch Omphale after his great labours, and spent his time spinning. The mystic Greek seer, Tieresias saw snakes copulating and was changed at that instant from a man to a woman. As a boy, Achilles was dressed as a girl by his mother; and identified himself as a boy when he chose a spear in place of a distaff.

The decadent Roman Emperor Heiloglobalus used to dress as a female often and went into the streets of Rome as a prostitute. His behaviour eventually became too much even for Rome in its decline, and he was assassinated.

Nero had a favourite, a boy, Sporus Sabina, castrated and dressed as a girl, because he resembled Nero's mother, for whom the Emperor had incestuous feelings.

St. Joan of Arc was burnt as a witch for dressing as a man. There were many women burnt as witches if they failed in some way to conform.

Queen Christina of Sweden dressed as a man, causing some scandal when she met the Pope. There is also the legend (or truth?) about Pope Joan.

The Chevalier d'Eon de Beaumont spied for France in Russia dressed as a woman. He was later required to live as a woman when he fled to England in order that he continue to receive his pension from the French King. He was a famous swordsman in Brighton, and in

Georgian England. At his death the betting as to which sex he was, stood at over a million pounds (1810).

The Abbé de Choisy dressed as a female, and even said Mass as a woman, became France's ambassador to Siam and wrote his memoirs, a splendid erotic mixture of fact, and a little fantasy. Louis XIV was quite sympathetic to transgenderists, his brother; Phillip Duc d'Orleans was probably one. Savalette de Langes lived as a woman at Court all 'her' life. The British Ambassador to New York, Viscount Cornbury scandalised the Yankees by wandering around New York dressed as a female. Henri III of France and his 'mignons' scandalised France by a mixture of cross-dressing and homosexuality.

Boulton and Park caused a scandal by prostitution and dressing in public as women quite convincingly in London (1871). In the eighteenth Century in London's notorious "Mollies Club," there was the cry of *"Tell me gentle hob decoy, art thou a girl or art thou a boy?"* England's first TV/TS club?

An archivist could go on and on. In more recent times there have been women who lived as men like Dr. James Miranda Barry, an army Surgeon General.

Many folk songs are filled with girls who "have gone to be a soldier." Vita Sackville-West, George Sand, Radclyffe Hall and many other women dressed as men.

In 1948, Michael Dillon had phalloplasty surgery to become the man he was. He became a ship's doctor, but later became a Buddhist monk.

In England Mark Rees in 1986 took his case to the European Court to try to get his birth certificate changed, his efforts were, sadly, not successful. Caroline Cossey - Tula - had a similar lack of success over the right to marry in 1988.

The earliest modern 'sex change' surgery for male to female we can trace is that of Lilli Elbe 1922 (once Hans Werner) in Denmark - an attempt was made at a genital and ovarian transplant. Later, and better known, are Christine Jorgensen who died in 1989, her surgery was in 1953, April Ashley, Cochinelle, Capucine (who killed herself in 1990), Amanda Lear, there's an ever growing list of personalities in showbiz who are TS …

The late Judy Cousins, who founded the Self-Help Association for Transsexuals, was a much-admired celebrity of the world of British TS's.

Adele Anderson, Wendy Carlos, Roberta Cowell, Amanda Lear, Stephanie Ann Lloyd, Angela Morley, Jan Morris, Fay Presto, Renee Richards, Dana Cohen, and many others have become well known personalities. In the nineties, the media are full of stories of Transexed people and their particular biographies, and all too often their stories are sensationalised.

There are, however, thousands of unknown stories of people who have escaped media exposure and got on with their lives quietly. What is interesting is that they are personalities in the first place and TS is only an aspect of their personality.

In the British area of legal influence April Ashley, a former Vogue model, is particularly significant. In 1970, her divorce outcome set a precedent, while remaining subject to various challenges, which caused the courts to make the marriage of a post-operative TS in the UK void, and the birth certificate issue a very real one. What is certain, is that there are, in the UK, thousands of private agonies, and quiet struggles, stories of great courage, and some, sadly, ending in misery or suicide.

Society itself is changing slowly, partly thanks to the work of **Press for Change** and other individuals, in challenging laws that deny human rights and natural justice. Media exposure, although often sensationalist has meant that there is some public understanding and sympathy for those with this difficulty.

There are many courageous men and women whose stories will not be told. There are many stories of couples staying together, of families coping and supporting one another, of these 'new' men and women finding life good and meaningful. After all the disadvantages there are such advantages. The overcoming of disability, the removal of this major distraction - life may take off as an exciting 'new birth', or renaissance, having grown through this pain.

It is not all pain and problems now if Nadia (Big Brother Winner 2004) is considered.

Having lived as both genders, the new men and women can be very much able to be men and women in the sense of standing against sexual stereotyping. There is a unique opportunity to challenge or to be peacemakers in the 'sex war' against the conditioned identities of men and women and to try to change fixed ideas of gender and stereotyping.

46

There may even be as many as 65,000 transsexuals in the UK, some went for surgery (about 6,000), others not. Some sought publicity, others had it thrust upon them. There are thousands of stories of quiet courage in facing these difficulties, concerning public perceptions and publicity as well as the internal battle.

23. Difficulties and Practicalities of Change.

A masculine or feminine body build does not affect the desire of the Gender Dysphoric person to present in the clothes and role of the other sex; it only enhances or damages that image. Sadly, some apparently physically very masculine 'males' desire, with as much conviction as a physically feminine man suffering from gender identity conflict, a gender resolution which may seem far from practical.

Society tends to judge women on their appearance. They are expected to conform to a stereotyped image and to look small, attractive and vulnerable. Post-operative 'new women' who do not match this image can never really integrate fully without some adverse comment. To seek surgery in that case (being "too tall, large boned etc. for a woman" - sizeism is another form of unacceptable discrimination). Surgery may resolve the inner problem, but leave an outer problem of simply never being able to 'pass'. Naturally this can cause great distress.

Very few big-boned or 'mannish' or tall women want to be men. There comes a point where a female who is Transexed, but is tiny and small-boned for a man, where her 'male image' would be so far from the usual spectrum of what a man 'should' look like. This frustrating situation can cause a real problem - you cannot yet grow six inches taller, develop larger or smaller bones.

Society itself is partly to blame here, for the old, tall or fat woman knows only too well the pressures to be a standard size, shape and image. Society seems based on images rather than actualities of personal identity. The effect of 'opposite-sex' hormones is to cause female to male TS's to undergo male-type puberty. They are fortunate in that facial hair will develop, the voice will break, and with an increase in musculature, they 'pass' relatively well, usually in a boyish way.

Being left with large bone structures, facial hair, deep voice, Adam's apple, large hands and feet, often hampers the MtF's. Oddly, sometimes a post-operative 'new-woman' retains some of the inbred (learnt) machismo of a man. Old habits die hard.

Alternatively, some may have such a stereotypical view of 'being a woman' that all they seem to aspire to is a view of themselves as feminine sex objects (if that is what they see a woman as), and there is little attempt to benefit from more liberated ideas of womanhood. A programme of unlearning has to be followed for real liberation to take place.

There is less guilt; it would seem, connected with being a female who is masculine, than being a male who is feminine. Sissies are not good news - are bullied at school and are shunned by most other children. Tomboys are, like Enid Blyton's "George", generally admired and approved of by their peer group and parents.

However in both MtF's and FtM's there is, initially, a great sense of isolation, inner turmoil, desperation and often depression. The depression reflects an inner suppression, and a sense of isolation. It is not an endogenous (from within) depression, but rather expresses the frustration felt because of The Big Secret, resulting from lack of sympathy or understanding from parents, media exposure, the law - and many medical 'experts' and psychiatrists.

This depression may derive from self-questioning and confusion resulting from the state of being a gender dysphoric person and is often reinforced by many recurring or common questions for which she or he can find no easy answer. Sometimes this dysphoria results in an agony of trying to conform to what is expected, if not demanded, by 'Society'.

Many hide this and keep a 'guilty secret'. Even after surgery the TS has not had an 'appropriate' childhood, or life history, so she or he has to invent one, or lie about it. To admit to it is often to bear the very real stigma of being a 'sex-change', instead of being regarded as a person who has overcome a disability. It seems there is no escaping the sense of difference and isolation some experience.

It seems that suicide rates among TS's are quite high pre-op. Even post-operatively, there seem to be so many practical problems to overcome in isolation. Many do overcome them, with or without surgery, and it is a testament to the indomitable human spirit that any survive as well-balanced happy people.

No problem is or, pragmatically, 'should be' your whole life. In a cognitive sense there is a chance of inner peace, but the emotions, which this condition arouses, do have to be faced and dealt with in a positive way. Ignorance, prejudice, isolation and despair itself are the real enemies of living more than half a life.

I am convinced that appropriate counselling before and after the physical problems have been resolved could do a great deal to help to reduce this suffering. Most medical and psychiatric conditions arouse some public sympathy, or at least some support from the family. Sadly this does not generally seem to be the experience of gender dysphoric people, who are seen as having perversely chosen this situation.

In Britain matters involving sex or gender are generally seen simply as black or white, with no idea that grey areas exist.

The realisation that sex is not either entirely male or female, that it is not simply a bipolar divide between people, but is a continuum, and that gender is also not simply bipolar, but a continuum, should help each of us to be less rigid about ourselves and others.

It is the intention of this book (as at the GENDYS Conferences) to provide a forum for discussion and thought. Hopefully much of the generalisation, mythology, and bad practice can give way to a more appropriate personalised, holistic and client-based form of treatment for people with these types of problems. Also the guilt, the prejudice and the ignorance can also be eroded for this type of person, who generally deserves acceptance, respect and understanding.

To be 'different' often means to suffer in our Society. Little help is available via the N.H.S, so many who can raise funds, "go private", and rush off to Thailand "for the snip", sometimes without a full preparation. This is a mistake, as many issues may possibly still need to be resolved, or post-operatively they will probably encounter these difficulties etc.

24. Order in a World where Gender or Sexual Polarity Cannot Clearly divide People.

Rather like Pythagoras 2.5k years ago, I do some of my thinking in the bath. The Pythagorean view, which Descartes extends - with all in its mathematical place, was an ordered world; in which status, sex, in fact all, was fixed, stratified and was made up of opposites and hierarchies. It was dipolar, as therefore was gender.

This ordered Cartesian (after Descartes 1596-1650) view, together with the spin off from Judeo-Christian concepts and Freudian psychology, has rather stifled ideas. These fixed ideas and divisions are challenged by the view that people cannot clearly be divided by Gender or Sexual Polarity, since each is a continuum, thanks to natural variation. Darwin and Wallace clearly stated that there is diversity, variation, and natural selection. Without variation or diversity there would be nothing from which to select and evolution would not have been possible.

Our species, like all mammals, reproduces by sexual reproduction. Sexual reproduction gives the genes almost infinite permutations, so no two individuals are absolutely identical, not even identical twins. Their experience of life and thought processes will have been separate. Each has an inherent individual identity, a name, and a separate existence. Diversity is to be celebrated as an opportunity for nature and for individuality.

25.   Passing successfully male to female (MtF).

In the strict sense there is a wide variety of sizes and shapes of women, not all are petite and beautiful. However, a man in a frock may look rather absurd, whilst a woman in a dinner suit can look really stunning - and still a woman.

The most usual mistake a trans woman (or a transvestite for that matter) makes, is perhaps to overdress, to dress tartily, to wear too much make-up, a dreadful rat of a wig, clothes more suitable for her/his mother - or her/his daughter.

All girls have to find their own style - what suits them - and more importantly what they feel comfortable wearing. That freedom is a little reversed in the MtF transgender mode. It is as well to get the advice of other women, that what you wear actually suits you. Long sleeves covering hairy arms or tattoos - no miniskirts if dreadful legs - use common sense. Mail order catalogues can supply your needs until you are confident. Jumble sales may mean you spend less but things might be very outmoded or unsuitable.

It is absurd to buy make-up or clothes from expensive specialist TV/TS shops, unless you want the 'Trannie look'. M&S and other Department stores can supply reasonable inexpensive products. Beauticians will sometimes advise in shops like Selfridges, Harrods etc.

if you have enough money and time for that sort of help. It is best, if possible, to use your own hair - styled properly to suit you - your face shape, and the colour should also be acceptable.

A helpful woman friend will be worth far more than a lot of expensive mistakes - women can objectively help each other in this way. It is a mistake to look better than your wife if you are married - and it is not morally justified to spend more on yourself as a woman, than on her or the family. Try to be fair! Pay cash if you haven't got changed-over credit cards and bank accounts - keep receipts so goods can be returned if required.

a) Voice Male voices break during puberty. They can not un-break. Female hormones do not lighten the voice and surgical attempts to modify the vocal chords can be dangerous and unreliable in some cases. Only a few reputable ENT specialists would offer a surgical solution based on the poor results so far obtained. Speech therapy and speech modification can help here.

There are many women with very deep voices (Dietrich, Bacall and many others). Speech therapists concentrate on raising the pitch, softening the quality and decreasing the resonance of the voice. Gendys Network can supply a list of Speech and Language Therapists skilled in this work if you contact the Website.

Men and women use somewhat different vocabularies. Women have a greater range of inflection and tend not to talk at a person, but to a person (unless greatly provoked!). Use a tape recorder and speech from the radio to try this out. There are videotapes available. Listen to women around you. It helps if you have the other person looking at you before you speak - your image may superimpose on the discord of the deep voice and the listener may discard the observation 'it's a man' in view of a good female presentation.

b) Body Language. Be careful not to give 'come on' messages (unless you mean to). Men have much more freedom of movement than women do. Men are fearful of aggressive women, yet if you are mouse-like they may feel you have something to hide. Gain confidence and believe in yourself. Only then will others believe in you.

c) Electrolysis and facial and body hair. Laser Treatment.
The eradication of the beard is one of the most important aspects of passing successfully. Unfortunately, hormone treatment does not

significantly affect beard growth, and other methods of permanent eradication have been employed. Two noteworthy failures in this direction are radiation and Depilex.

At effective dosage levels radiation treatment carries the possible risk of skin cancer and subcutaneous scars at some later date, while at acceptable dosage levels the loss of beard growth is often only temporary. In addition it is an expensive procedure and for these reasons radiation treatment is rarely used.

Depilex is a relatively recent innovation. A current is applied to a pair of tweezer-like electrodes, which grip the hair at its base. It is claimed that the current passes down the hair to its root. However, this form of hair removal is always under tension and one Consultant Dermatologist has, after eighteen months of experiments in conjunction with an electrologist, dismissed this method as no more than expensive plucking. In fairness, one should add that the manufacturers and distributors of this equipment do not claim permanent removal of hair.

At present, the only proven method of permanent beard removal for all is needle electrolysis, technically known as short-wave diathermy.

Laser treatment for beard and/or blemish removal is established in several good clinics, but it is perhaps a little early to say whether there are financial advantages in this form of hair removal. A real disadvantage is that Laser Treatment is very effective for black hair, but will not work on blond, red or grey hair. In Clinical trials it has been used to clear donor skin from the scrotal area prior to GRS. After the op' it is important that hair does not grow in the neovagina.

In time there may be a simple, painless and fast way of permanent hair removal, but for now it is a long drawn out, time consuming, irritating, often painful and invariably expensive process, sometimes more expensive than surgery.

Patients seeking gender reassignment privately think in terms of psychiatric and surgical costs of £4,000 to £9,000 plus, but many patients, both NHS and private, overlook the fact that beard removal may well often cost nearly as much again. Current cost of needle electrolysis is £10.00 to £25.00 or more per hour, and treatment is very rarely obtainable under the NHS.

In the process of needle electrolysis, a special machine produces heat at the tip of a needle which has been inserted into the hair follicle to the depth of the hair root. This briefly burns the root and the hair can then be removed without tension. In a small percentage of cases, this hair will have been permanently killed, but most hairs require anything from two to seven insertions before the root has been completely eradicated and regrowth ceases.

The main factors affecting the period of treatment required are: the age of the client, which often determines the strength of hair growth; the straightness or otherwise of the hair in the follicle, which may be distorted by previous plucking, either of which may require the operator to reduce the power during treatment, and of course the skill and speed of the electrologist.

An experienced operator averages 500-600 hairs per hour; slower operators may only average 300 per hour. For a light beard, a full course of treatment might take eighteen months: a more likely period is two to three years for a medium or heavy growth.

Needle electrolysis is a procedure, which requires careful training. If it is clumsily employed there is a real danger of scarring. For this reason care should be taken in choosing an experienced professional operator. Limiting electrolysis to about two hours a week will allow at least six days for any epidermal inflammation or soreness to subside and heal.

Plainly higher charges do not necessarily mean more skilful treatment. It is advisable to obtain continuity of treatment from the same operator. At present many electrolysis clinics refuse to treat 'men', while others require a referral from a doctor.

For electrolysis to take place, it is necessary to stop shaving for two to three days prior to the session. This can pose serious problems for the transexed person living and working as a woman. Therefore it is strongly advised to begin electrolysis as early as possible, well before social reassignment takes place.

Moreover, it is also recommended that electrolysis be completed prior to gender reassignment surgery. For, post-operatively, the emotional hazards of having to shave whilst adjusting to a new-body image can cause problems.

Even after the major work has been done, it may be necessary to see your electrologist at infrequent intervals to remove regrowth to those hairs previously dormant.

In the case of boys who are definitely gender dysphoric there seems to be good justification in allowing them to take puberty-arresting medication to prevent beard growth and the voice breaking. This procedure is possible in the Netherlands with parental agreement, and saves the child so many of the difficulties of male puberty. It is apparently reversible.

With regard to the provision of electrolysis treatment under the NHS, the DSS has, on 30th September 1981, in a letter from the Joint Parliamentary Under Secretary of State, written:

"I am sorry if your constituent has been wrongly advised that this treatment is not available on the NHS, as this is not the case. Electrolysis treatment may be made available under the NHS in individual cases where it has been prescribed as clinically necessary by a consultant. It is important that such decisions should be left to the clinical judgement of doctors, and we would not wish to change such an arrangement."

"I should just explain that it is not always possible to provide sufficient facilities and staff in NHS hospitals so that this may be undertaken directly by health service electrologists. Where this is the case, arrangements may be made by the Authority for such treatment to be provided by recognised practitioners acceptable to the consultant and able to carry out the prescription. The decision by the health authority whether or not to arrange treatment is of course for the authority to decide in the light of local resources and other priorities and if arranged outside the NHS is subject to the Department's approval"

It is of course each trans woman's responsibility to pursue his case for NHS electrolysis individually through his own consultant and GP.

26.   Passing successfully female to male (FtM).

a) Voice. The situation with a FtM person is similar in certain ways, but unlike the MtF, taking so-called opposite-sex hormones, it has effects, which are not reversible, even over a relatively short time-scale. The voice can not un-break - a beard and a hairy body don't just go, once androgenisation is stopped, so clinicians need to be absolutely certain that the treatment is appropriate in these cases than with their MtF sisters.

After hormone treatment, the FtM trans-man will usually have a deeper masculine voice, which will have broken - a beard, and masculine body hair. There is often a tendency to put on weight as fat, but with exercise this can help achieve masculine body musculature and outline.

54

b) Height. Nothing can be done about the originally female bone structure, which is often small in terms of hands, feet and height. So if you were a small person, you will remain a small person. Because of a more 'female' skin tone there will be a tendency to look younger than the average male of the same age. In addition there is the problem of creating a boyhood or having to be honest with people.

Some trans-men may over compensate, as small men often do (Sorry! I'm stereotyping!). They may become rather pushy and sensitive about their height. Quite gentle men do exist and you will probably find you are under less scrutiny if you can find a balance between being too pushy or too shy. Show confidence and be yourself.

c) Bodyshape. Pre-mastectomy, the breasts will need to be disguised, either by using a flattening bandage (e.g. crêpe bandage), or by wearing thick shirts or waistcoats with large breast pockets. A rolled up sock in jockey briefs can be used to give a realistic trouser bulge.

A man can now create his own style. There is a danger in the initial stages of looking or behaving over aggressively. Most trans men will find that they pass in public without any trouble, though using the male toilet can present problems if phalloplasty has not been performed. There are, however, devices, which can be purchased or made to help with urinary flow when using a urinal.

Acne, endured by many boys as they pass through puberty, is often encountered during the early stages of Testosterone treatment. This should eventually clear up.

Most of these new men see male pattern baldness as an advantage as it reinforces the fact they are like most other men. A large proportion of these men grows a beard and takes up traditional masculine hobbies and sports.

* *The White Book* by S.T. Whittle PhD, from FTM Network London WC1N3XX, is a good reference

27. Where To Get Help - How to Cope with Legal and Administrative Matters.

Citizen's Advice Centres are a good source of information. So is the Internet. There are documents, which should prove helpful during changeover.

It should not be necessary to have to provide anything to express your name/gender change to billing companies, simply tell them henceforth the account will be paid by …*(new Name)*… Banks are a little more difficult and will want (confidentially to the Manager) a copy Statutory Declaration and new Signature samples, or you could have opened an account at your bank earlier in your new name.

Where justification of your new role and dress code is required (Employment offices, driving offences for example), your identity can be confirmed by having a Doctor's letter.

The problem of the transexed person tends, because of its surgical resolution, to be one which is addressed by the family doctor in the first instance. Whatever, the GP, or private doctor, makes a referral to a specialist (preferably at a GIC like Charing Cross Hospital) - or privately if the waiting list for NHS clinics is too long.

If, in the view of the specialist, the patient is, or may be TS, the GP will then have a letter requesting repeat prescriptions for hormones. The GP may then be requested to be kind enough to provide a letter as shown below. Of course, prior to obtaining this certificate, you should agree your changeover date with all concerned and change your name by Statutory Declaration. This will help in amending other documents.

Doctor's Letter

"To whom it may concern:

This is to confirm that my patient (Mr.,/Miss/Ms./Mrs.) (Full name) is currently undergoing gender reassignment to the (female/male) role, and as part of this process has changed (his/her) name by Statutory Declaration to (Mr./Miss) (Full name).

Your assistance in making the relevant changes in your records and in preserving full confidentiality would be appreciated.

Signed: .... (General Practitioner).   Dated: ...."

At an earlier stage, you might benefit from a Consultant's letter (from the Consultant or GP if you are known to your doctor as bona fide).

Some consultant psychiatrists will provide, on request, suitable patients with a letter, as shown below. This may help on occasions. It is not a carte blanche to behave stupidly, but does provide an element of security for the frightening early stages of changing documentation and gaining self-confidence, and with some employers etc.

You can use this with your Statutory Declaration to get a new Driving Licence or a Passport can also be organised confidentially in your current name and Gender, see later.

Gender Identity Clinic - Consultant's Letter:

> *"Date* .... *Medical Ref. No.* .... *X Hospital address*
>
> *GENDER IDENTITY CLINIC*
>
> *This card is to indicate that (name, e.g. Francis(es) Everidge is attending the Gender Identity Clinic at this hospital for assessment for the condition of Gender Dysphoria (transsexualism) and if it is appropriate for him/her to wear female/male clothes as part of the treatment, confirmation can be obtained by contacting the Dept of Psychiatry at ....*
> *Hospital.*
>
> *Patient's Signature ....F.E....   Consultant ....Dr.X.... Signature"*

28.   To Formalise a Name Change using a Statutory Declaration.

This is cheaper than a Deed Poll. You can swear it (have it witnessed) before an officer of the Court or a solicitor. An example is shown on the next page.

Keep several copies - never send the original. It is a matter of preference if you keep the same surname, initials etc. If you want to change some documents you may need to send a photocopy of Birth Certificate (which can not be changed as yet), the Statutory Declaration (and a letter from the GIC if you like). If you make your own you save money. Get it sworn (£5 approx) before a solicitor or Clerk of the Court.

29.   Other Documents.

Send copies, if possible, *not originals,* of your own documents regarding your changeover.

a) Medical Card/Records. Send a note to your doctor or psychiatrist - or write yourself, with photocopies of Statutory Declaration, the old medical card and a doctor's letter and get the Local Family Practitioners Committee to change your medical card and records. You can request

STATUTORY DECLARATION

I ....(Old name)...................

Of ....(Address)...............

DO SOLEMNLY AND SINCERELY DECLARE as follows:

1. I absolutely and entirely renounce, relinquish and abandon the use of my former names of ....Old name........................ *and assume adopt and determine to take and use the names of* ....New name.......... *in substitution for my former names of* ....Old name..............

2. I shall at all times hereafter in all records deeds documents and other writings and in all actions proceedings as well as in all dealings and transactions on all occasions whatsoever use and subscribe the said names of

...........New name............... *as my name in substitution for my former names of* ....Old name............... *so relinquished as aforesaid to the intent that I may hereafter be called known or distinguished not by my former names of*

.............Old name .... *but by my names of* ....New name .... *only.*

3. I authorise and require all persons at all times to designate describe and address me by the adopted names of ....New name...........

4. AND I make this solemn Declaration conscientiously believing the same to be true and by virtue of the provisions of the Statutory Declarations Act 1835.

SIGNED & DECLARED at ....MX Court or Solicitor's address.... *in the County of* ....MX.......

This Mon./Tues./..*day, the* .....nth...... *of* ......month........, ...full year e.g. 2005.........

Witnessed Before me, Solicitor/ Commissioner for Oaths ....

58

to see your medical records and ask for a summary record to be appended to your new card rather than show the doctor's secretary the whole story in the file quite so obviously.

b) Income Tax Files and Records. Send a copy of the Statutory Declaration and the medical card with a covering letter. They will be changed. Always write to a senior officer confidentially to avoid any unnecessary publicity.

c) Bank Accounts/Post Office/Building Society Savings Accounts/Share Certificates. Simply change the name on them, backed up by your Statutory Declaration, or change your banking to a new Account. The Manager can deal it with confidentially.

Do not forget to get the name changed on your Premium Bonds and Savings Certificates if you have any.

d) Pensions. It is important to confidentially ensure any existing pensions owned by you have the name amended. Write to a manager with proof of name change. You do not need to give any further explanation other than a Statutory Declaration.

e) National Insurance Office and DSS files. The same applies - the record can be summarised and a new file created with only a senior supervisor having access to your full file. You should write confidentially to the National Office, and mark your request to the Senior Supervisor of Records. Request that the computerised records and Branch Office computer screens will also be secure and not state other than your name and the gender you live as now.

The DSS will not normally change your National Insurance Number, since this links into retirement and pension age.

f) Driving Licence. Send a photocopy of your Statutory Declaration, and medical card and re-apply in your new name. Ask for a new female number (if you are M to F), or vice versa. Write to the DVLC, Swansea - confidential.

Your date of birth and sex is shown in the number, as follows.

A man born on the Seventh of June 1943 would have a number 406073 so 4-----3-year-0---- sex, --6--- month and ---07-date. A female would be shown as 456073.

g) Utilities and Insurance Companies. Get your name changed with the Utilities and Services such as telephone, electricity, gas, water, TV Licence, Driving and Household Insurance, Vehicle Registration

59

Documents, etc. Having cleared all outstanding bills, you can change the person named on the bill by a simple letter stating your 'new name' who will be responsible for these bills in future.

h) Electoral Registration. This is concerned with one-person one vote, not names.

Simply send a letter with the new name, or, when making the annual return simply write the new, rather than the old, name. Do not vote as 'another person'.

i) Property. For those who own property or land, have the name on the Land Registry changed.

j) Life and Medical Insurance. Insurance companies may ask for a lifestyle questionnaire to be completed. This can present real problems. It may be wise to consider a new form of cover, using an agent to find the best deal.

k)A caution for Divorcees. If all documentation is changed before a divorce you may get a situation of Mrs. Bloggs vs. Miss Bloggs in the divorce hearing.

l) Exam Certificates and Qualifications can be changed, as can registration with professional bodies. There are sometimes small charges made for this service. It may be a good idea to get references in your new name.

m) Passports. The passport office will consider an application for change of name on its merits. Send a letter from your medical advisor, one from yourself, and a copy of the Statutory Declaration. Write to The Supervisor of Passports in your National Office, mark your letter "Most Confidential". Ask for any original documents to be returned.

n) A Will and other Loose Strands. These can be important and easily forgotten. Remember if you have loose ends of any type, a Will, for example, you should consider them at this point. It is sensible if you specify what you wish. Do you want to be buried/cremated under your actual (chosen) name and gender? Do you wish to have your name recorded on a headstone for example? Ensure that your Will protects your wishes concerning your partner, significant friends, children and so on. It is worth getting all these matters sorted out properly so mistakes do not occur. See a solicitor if necessary.

If you regard these changes as getting a new life, it is wise to use this time to sort out all the details of life and get things in order. The bureaucracy of a change over is a good test of your resolve.

30.   Relationships.

Relationships from the emotional perspective of both the TS person and the partner during changeover and post-operatively.

Trans people often become absorbed with their dysphoria. Moving to their hopefully more euphoric post-operative state, their expectations can be unrealistic, and relationships may suffer. Further, there is often both a great sense of relief having post-op' achieved as near as possible their goal. This is followed sometimes by a void, and the practical realisation that they are alone, although they may be at-one with self physically and emotionally.

Some take off on a 'delayed adolescence'. Others feel a sort of 'let down'. The lack of any real follow up by GIC's means that the TS is sometimes barely prepared emotionally for her or his new life, is often lonely, and has no great goal left in life.

Whether before or throughout the surgical confirmation process the TS may be married, or have either a heterosexual or homosexual partner. For them the shock of discovering the person they love is going to become someone who is physically very different is enormous. They may well react in various ways: anger, hostility, frustration, bitterness, isolation, or in some cases optimism.

They will usually feel hurt and sometimes blame themselves, wondering if they lack anything, if it's their fault or that they may have somehow caused the changes within their partner.

Some partners are at first supportive, but find the reality of the change impossible to cope with. In all cases much understanding, patience and talking is needed. It is essential that all decisions that could challenge the relationship, which are made by the TS, be made with the knowledge of their partner.

In most cases partners do not stay together after surgery, and it is as much the attitude of the partner as that of the TS which determines the attitude of the children and family. Some TS's seem very self-focused and often may seem selfish and even ruthless, and this causes suffering to those around them.

She or he has good reason to fight for self-realisation, but the two dynamics of self and love are often opposing. Often great anguish exists for the partner and for the TS. Partners can be concerned that their children's own gender identity development may be adversely affected

61

by a change over. There is no apparent evidence to support this, although there can be a profound distress.

Often depression exists before diagnosis is made. If self-realisation is not possible, this in itself can be very destructive. The depression resulting from repressed feelings of gender identity conflict may result in negativity, bad moods and broken homes and relationships.

A compromise is necessary. In an acrimonious divorce, or any row, whether formalised by divorce or not, these difficulties can be worsened for all concerned by unthinking and deliberate blame-placing.

A refusal to refer to a former partner by their new identity and name can be very hurtful, and can confuse children. Very young children seem to adapt quite easily, but it seems that, for pre-adolescent and adolescent children, it is more difficult. However individual children's responses will vary within a family.

Above all it is important for them to realise that they still have two parents who care about them and love them. The extraordinary in a family may cause problems for those who are conventional; however extraordinary strengths can be found in a family's solidarity.

The great fear of 'what will the neighbours or family or friends think?' is often uppermost in a partner's mind. For it is usually the partner not the TS who has to answer all the very awkward and embarrassing questions.

For some families, moving home has solved some of these problems. Others may have the confidence of their love for their TS partner to ride out any problems; for some it is all just too much. Whatever the circumstances of a changeover, once 'reassignment' or 'confirmation' has occurred, a whole new (and sometimes both exciting and frightening) world opens up.

Male to female TS's might well feel that they wish to prove their womanhood as rapidly as possible, post-operatively, by having sexual intercourse with a man. This can be either wonderful or disappointing for them, the first sexual experience for the TS may well be painful and sore, with little feeling and no orgasm, but this can happen for any woman virgin. Nervousness and a lack of lubrication (save seminal fluid from the prostate) and a possible lack of nerve endings in the new vagina, means that vaginal orgasm is not assured. Orgasm may occur because the new woman feels a physical confirmation of her femaleness, rather than a physical response to having actually having been penetrated. Much sexual pleasure is between the ears, not just between the legs.

Vaginal orgasm in the MtF TS is also possible because of the stimulation of the prostate gland, which remains in situ. If the surgeon has left a penile stump it can be a problem in sex, if it's too long it's painful, it expands with excitement, and also it doesn't look right. Clitoral orgasm is preferred by some women, and is an option for these trans women. Making love with your partner is much more beautiful and important than just having sex. The majority of MtF TS's is heterosexual and with good fortune have fulfilment in this sort of relationship.

In up to 30% of post-operative MtF TS's, there may be a realisation that they are not sexually attracted or satisfied by men as lovers, and they need the emotional fulfilment that a lesbian relationship can provide for them. This can come as something of a shock, or a delightful surprise.

A wife who has stood by her partner and remains with her post-operatively may feel their friendship is threatened if the TS is too uncaring in seeking a sexual partner, if she can not relate sexually because she is not a lesbian herself. Such an ex-wife may see herself as a sort of sister, but definitely not as a lesbian lover. Love takes many forms beyond the realms of sexual expression. TS's often define themselves by their genitals, rather than by what is between their ears. Once surgery is complete they often feel an anti-climax. Relationships become more important again.

The majority of female to male TS's is heterosexual, and nearly all their lives have sought a female partner, so their sexual preference remains the same. A partnership that began as lesbian becomes heterosexual. This can cause difficulty for that partner in defining her own sex role, since she will already have had to come to terms with being a lesbian.

TS's are often very stereotypical, fortunately not all are. Couples can reach their own understanding, and a system or relationship which works for them.

There is clearly a different sexual element between a post-operative TS and their partner, in the FtM transexed person whether there has been a phalloplasty or not, and in the post-operative MtF TS.

A female to male can have the advantage of understanding how a woman's body works, and often is very able to satisfy his partner. Some TS's gain satisfaction in the pleasure of their partner, and that is enough.

An effect of Testosterone is to enlarge the clitoris and may greatly increase the sexual libido. Often a clitoris treated as a penis (rubbed) when stimulated can produce very satisfactory orgasms. No phalloplasty as yet can produce a natural erection in the pseudo-penis. It is necessary to use 'technology' to gain an erect phallus for penetration, which is important for some heterosexual FtM men.

Many of these men have fulfilling sexual relationships based on intimate knowledge of the bodies and minds of their partner. Some have homosexual relations, and will integrate into that community. Transhomosexuality is beginning to be understood.

For the post-operative TS of whichever direction and whatever their sexual preference or preferences, safe sexual practices, in both the heterosexual and homosexual communities should be observed, because of the prevalence of AIDS and other sexually transmitted diseases and infections. Partners may have fear of AIDS if the solution to their relationship is an 'open' relationship. Consideration is not only important, it is vital here.

Even post-operatively the TS will face the problem of telling their new lover. It is confusing for the person being told, and even traumatic to have to perhaps revise a perception of a lover as someone who was physically different in their past. Some partners will question their own sexuality, and suffer the fears of the need to be conventional. They have a need for reassurance. Their own heterosexuality or homosexuality or lesbianism is not in fact in question, nor need that of their partners be so.

Many post-operative TS's believe they should not tell their partner about their past. If a partner finds out, this may be more damaging. The key to a successful relationship is tactful honesty and consideration. One of the greatest traumas for a post-operative TS is having to explain, often fearfully, their background to the person they love. Clearly for some women involved in feminist or lesbian groups this background could cause great problems, and in a heterosexual situation the fact that she can't have children is sometimes important.

Discretion on the part of friends who know and of partners is essential in all cases.

64

Families, parents, brothers, sisters, children and other relatives will all react in a variety of ways to the TS. They must be given time, for they will need it, to accept or reject the situation.

31. Marriage and a Transperson - (If Marriage was Before Change-over).

Many TS's do marry, having tried to make a go of 'normal' life in their prescribed gender role. My research shows that roughly a third of (MtF) TS's marry. It is less usual for an FtM to do so.

The gender motivated MtF TS is usually 'heterosexual' that is to say sexually attracted to women rather than men. In his original life role, he may place women in an idealised position, and may for some, oscillate between this and jealousy, which may be acute. There are often mood swings, which seem to improve if the TS is 'given his way'.

However, a wife or female partner may feel she gets little from this 'bargain' herself and often sees their relationship/marriage threatened. She feels she is losing her husband, feels betrayed, feels to blame, feels challenged. She is often fearful of the effect of cross-gender manifestations on the children, if they have any, on his employment and money worries, the rest of the family and the ubiquitous critical neighbours.

It can present challenges to her womanhood, to her sexuality and her own identity, as well as possibly severely destabilising an otherwise good relationship. Few TS's will have told a wife of the situation, some genuinely did not know themselves for certain prior to the marriage. Many want children and family life.

A decision for reassignment can only be reached after much discussion with a wife or husband. Some couples do stay together through this, and a few wives remain in situ as best friends or 'sisters' with their ex-husband.

It is usual for the GIC's to expect that there be no existing marriage, for fear of a litigating outraged wife. However various waivers can be signed if this decision to acquiesce is acceptable to a spouse.

There can be great burdens on a spouse, who will simply see the man she loves both ceasing to be a man, and growing away. Moreover, that as a 'woman' she is happy about this 'progress away'. It often results in an unhappy ending of the relationship for a wife who may feel her own femininity and sense of self worth threatened.

It is unfair to conceal hormone therapy from a partner. Sexual libido suffers as well as other physical changes - and this can put a strain on the sexual activity in a marriage or relationship.

No trans person can obtain, or indeed in the author's view, should obtain surgery, either NHS or privately, without a written recommendation from a psychiatrist and a second opinion. Usually the patient is expected to be single under civil law (see Standards of Care), however there are cases where a signed agreement to the surgery from the spouse will suffice if the marriage is to continue.

A result of the Gender Recognition Act 2004 is that the spouse who was Transexed should either not apply for a Gender Recognition Certificate, as it would render the marriage void (or the Certificate void). A careful decision must be made as to the priority, the marriage or the Recognition. It is hard for these couples who want to stay married.

Sometimes after the changeover it is possible for new woman and ex-wife to become good friends, given time. Much understanding is due to each partner, and to the children.

32.   Children of a Transperson.

It is clear that children need certainty, stability and honesty, and they are very adaptable. If there is a great deal of acrimony, hostility, blame placing openly in the home, and a painful divorce, they may be required by either or both parents to take sides. This is painful to them and should be avoided if possible.

Very young children seem more able to accept the situation. Children within a family vary in a range of reactions from absolute rejection to enthusiastic acceptance of their changed-over parent. There is no evidence of a family trait towards transsexualism. Some teenage boys in particular might feel fearful that they have a tendency (albeit latent) towards transsexualism - a young male needs the role model of a Dad to challenge and develop his own identity. He may well worry about his peer group's reaction to his having a 'trannie' dad. Younger children do, it seems, adapt best.

If divorce occurs there are often problems with custody and access. It is important that both parents do try, if they can, to resolve their own legal arrangements without dragging the children into any rows that may occur. If possible children should not be pawns in a game involving blame, because this will damage them.

In these cases her ex-husband is seen by the ex-wife as the 'other woman', so it is not surprising that acrimony can evolve, often fuelled by the lawyers, and doubts in the court's mind that the new-woman will have a suitable effect on the children.

In any divorce the one thing that can be said is that the love that remains, is usually that from each parent for the children. No longer as a family, but with parents working together for their children's common good. This gives the best chance of stability and security. It is important to show the children they are loved just as much as ever by both parents.

Divorce is not easy for either partner, and it should not be forgotten that it is hard for the children even without the added dimension of having a TS parent. Children should surely be told with tact and care of their parent's Gender Dysphoria.

A joint, caring approach is best so far as children are concerned, with both parents confronting the problems rather than each other. Children have often shown that they can assimilate quite dramatic events without being unduly disturbed or adversely affected, provided all concerned co-operate for the child's best interests. Much depends on the attitude of the spouse.

One of the few published comments comes from Dr. Fisk of the USA, *"In terms of children, my own experience has been that there have not been any significant or profound psychological aberrations in children whose parent has undergone gender re-orientation."*

The British Courts are very conservative, particularly in Custody and Access matters. Before a divorce hearing it is wise to seek suitable professional help, such as trained counselling (e.g. Relate). Bitterness and rancour should be minimised. The Legal system sets people up as protagonists, and not enough emphasis is put on conciliation.

For the children's sake a united approach is less traumatic. They must neither be told nor asked to take sides. Judges and registrars seem to have an abhorrence of anything perceived by them as abnormal or 'irrational' and this 'Legal View' would seem to be far behind those of Medicine or Public Opinion.

The TS parent frequently feels, and is, as disadvantaged as much as the gay parent is. Transvestites, transsexuals, lesbians, or gay men all appear to be regarded with the same disdain as junkies, alcoholics, abusers or the violent by the courts.

In theory each case is seen on its merits, and a good, but 'eccentric' parent is sometimes seen as a better option than putting a child into care.

If possible, if separation has occurred, regular access arrangements should be agreed and installed before the final hearing. Keep an accurate record of the access, photos of children with the TS parent apparently happy together if possible and hope you have an enlightened Court Welfare Officer (Social Worker). Psychiatric evidence in support will help the court, which may order this anyway.

It is wise not to make a fuss about being TS, or to minimise it. Others might make a fuss. Normally the divorce hearing is in Chambers unless it goes to appeal, and this should keep the press uninvolved. It is possible that opposing council, or solicitor, may try to goad the TS as an attempt to demonstrate that she or he is unsuitable as a parent solely because she or he is a TS.

It is wise to understand that the condition and its consequent social problems do pose a real problem to other people, not least the spouse. A child's needs must and do come first. If stability can be demonstrated there is some chance an enlightened judgement may result, in respect of custody and access. All divorcees should surely be prepared to try to find a compromise, which is realistic and compassionate to all parties.

Be prepared for ruthless cross-examination if access or custody are being contended, and do not oscillate between gender roles (i.e. male/female presentation) it is better to appear as a convincing man or woman in your role choice. Do not leave it to unpleasant speculation by the judge as to what sort of parody of a person he might assume you to be. The court has to be convinced that you will not bring derision on the children, or itself, so be both practical and courageous.

Despite this, there have been well known cases both in the UK and the USA, where a judge has even required a post-operative TS to dress up as a member of their original gender to see the children. This seems particularly inhumane, and reduces the TS to the status of an 'it'. One barrister has described custody in TS cases as a steady drip, drip, away at a block of granite.

As the legal system gains experience and more favourable precedents are set, the quite abhorrent and apparent discrimination against TS's is being eroded gradually. Even if, sadly, estrangement occurs with the children, time is a healer. Sometimes, given time, forgiveness takes place and children and changed-over parents become close again.

The law has stability, the child's welfare, and provision for the child as its main goals. It will not, even if very sympathetic to an individual TS, place his or her interests above those of the children. There have been cases of custody going to a TS parent, and access has been quite usual. Current legislation does not make use of the terms 'custody' and 'access', but 'responsibility'.

33.   Counselling - How Then, Can the Therapist or Counsellor Help her/his Client?

It is my belief that the Client Leads in Effective Gender Counselling. It is damaging to a client if a counsellor tries to act as gatekeeper, as someone who has, as a goal, to get all her clients into surgery, or to prevent this. The counsellor or psychotherapist must not work to a personal agenda, but needs to facilitate and to listen.

Humans are complex, multidimensional individuals and their counselling is to help them through a difficulty or series of problems, to find a way of being which is comfortable, practical and life enhancing. Not to seek and have any effective counselling is to invite later problems. Some clients feel and need long-term counselling. Others seek counselling as a form of crisis intervention, or to help them to think through what they want to do, can do, or will do, about their gender identity conflict, or whatever issues may arise connected with this in themselves or their loved ones.

34.   What is the Role, Purpose or Goal of Counselling?

My experience is that counselling in the context of gender dysphoria will be at its most helpful if it is both cognitive and eclectic. We are not dealing with a mental illness, but with an unease about lifestyle, body and personality, together with the spin-off produced by a critical society and the consequent guilt trips felt by those who are victimised by this hostile attitude.

In "Client led" counselling I would suggest the client will describe what he or she feels. The counsellor's task is to assist the client towards finding what the actual problem may be, and consider how this could be addressed. In doing so the client grows less confused by the layers of feelings and more able to resolve the difficulty.

It is important to challenge irrational beliefs and involve a client in being informed and taking personal responsibility. A client is invited to engage their mind as well as their feelings towards finding a way of being which is acceptable, possible and practical for his or her lifestyle. This process can be rapid or protracted, but does mean that the client has a fuller understanding of her or his feelings, goals and solutions. The client needs to weigh up emotional and practical cost to self and others against benefits.

35. The Need for Personal Therapy and Counselling.

The first task of a person who feels gender dysphoric is to establish as far as possible where they are in the various spectra of gender, sexuality and sex. They need to establish what the medics term a diagnosis. They might simply enjoy the clothes of the other gender. They might have fetishistic tendencies. It could be they are gay or bisexual. Most importantly they may need to engage brain as well as emotions and look carefully and cognitively at their situation in terms of self, loved ones and others around them and think about what could be possible, real and a full part of their life. Self-acceptance is important. Often a person who has any degree of gender confusion or mutability feels great guilt, isolation and shame because of the prohibitions placed on all if they do not conform to 'normality'.

Therapy does not imply any madness, but can help with confusion of thought, especially when dealing with emotions and confusion, guilt and lack of other to talk about the problem.

We might hope that the client goes on to find what sort of (hopefully) liberated woman or man or androgyne she or he actually is or can be. I mean by this that the greatest changes are brought about in recognising the situation, learning self-acceptance, and gaining the acceptance of others. It means dealing with the consequent social changes and coping with the emotional, practical and social problems that may arise during and after this changeover, and above all learning to be oneself. This also applies if surgery is not a practical option or really wanted.

Gender dysphoria is not a mental illness, but a variation or predisposition. It has great significance in terms of identity, resulting in social repercussions, which are often drastic or catastrophic.

Gender Confirmation is as much social as personal, about personality, as much as about what sort of body you have.

Since an aim surely is towards self-liberation it is also important that the individual can escape from stereotyping. As the process of reassignment is one in which the inappropriate gender is rejected, it is important that the client realises that women and men today need not be confined to interests and skills which were sex/gender defined, in other words they can be themselves.

She can mend cars, he can be a gentle man, she can hate housework and he can love it. To be a whole person, a major adjustment comes with the realisation that self-stereotyping is confining. Nobody need become a 'typical' man or woman, each can be multidimensional and therefore a more real personality.

I believe that the Standards of Care have failed to recognise this and provide realistic support in this difficult process. The Real Life Test can often be a real nightmare. It places the client in a physical and, to an extent, emotional limbo. It should not be over long. This can only cause damage, without any counselling or psychotherapeutic support.

This gap in support is to a small extent met by the various support groups. Their work is barely recognised by many professionals. I believe that a more person-centred approach might produce better therapeutic results. There seems to be a sense in which the patient has to fit a particular set of criteria, which are often unrelated to the standards of care, or to the real needs of that person.

We can appreciate that the transferences involved in seeing a psychiatrist about a matter as important as gender identity can produce a high degree of dysfunction, in parent/child dynamics. Patients are tempted to lie to clinicians to give the 'right answers' to get what they want.

What the patient actually needs against what she or he wants can be very different.

Certainly there is a place for counselling in most cases.

36. The NHS and Private Medicine/Psychiatry - Few Resources and Long Waiting Lists.

The task of psychiatrists is to ensure that a gender dysphoric person will be helped by any treatment offered. Surgery is almost impossible to reverse, so caution must be exercised in offering it. But do waiting lists, once a person has qualified for surgery, have to be so long?

The Standards suggest the life-test should be a year. Usually several years are spent "in-role" prior to going to a G.I.C. This time seems to be disregarded by the G.I.C.'s, and with a shortage of good experienced surgeons, the waiting list may be several years long. In the U.K. there are several "Gender Identity Clinics". There is one overloaded G.I.C. at Charing Cross Hospital which handles the vast majority of cases, and several much smaller centres.

We need more experienced and qualified surgical specialists in this type of work. We also need more good regional G.I.C.'s to avoid this C.X overload.

37. Funding Problems and Consequences.

Although there are mechanisms in place in the Health Service, it seems we do not take advantage of the surgery being offered in the Netherlands, Belgium or elsewhere as a means of reducing this waiting list.

Isn't this a wasted opportunity? Whatever happened to Bevan's Health Service, or the Patient Charter for that matter? Few of us believe that the real-life-test should last any more than the Standards of Care state as necessary. It places an intolerable strain on the patient to be in a sort of sex/gender limbo. If he or she has money this can be overcome by going 'private'.

Geography should not define care, nor in an ideal world should resources. Where you live can affect funding as to local policy and availability of those funds.

Several G.P. Practices and Area Health Authorities have introduced rationing, with waiting lists and all sorts of excuses (like "this is cosmetic or elective surgery!"). Since the suicide rate is unknown, but certainly high, I feel sure that elective death (suicide), or oblivion using drink or drugs, or depressive illness and breakdown, is a consequence. In fact the system loses many by this so-called 'natural wastage'. No effective audit has been carried out on treatment regimes for those who were given surgery, let alone those who did not want it or were refused it.

Actually the benefits of having regional centres of excellence would I believe produce cost-effective, profitable, units around the country, and the savings to the nation in prevention of these malaises caused by ignoring the problem could be demonstrated.

38.   Age and the Constraints of Chronology.

Assignment at birth and replacement birth certificates sometimes has always taken place for some intersexed babies, but what of errors in gender identity? When we look at paediatric medicine there is still the problem of children with unclear or ambiguous sex organs or chromosomes being assigned at birth, before their actual gender is defined.

It seems that the parents and not the child are treated by assigning and surgical interventions. The concerns of the parents make it a medical emergency to assign a sex to the newborn baby. Surgery is performed on babies on anatomical grounds without thought for the future Gender Identity of that child. Young transexed patients who present have at least got a clinic in London (The Portman Clinic) and one in the Netherlands, where it may be possible for puberty to be retarded until they are old enough to proceed with a suitable resolution of their dysphoria. "Mermaids" offers emotional support to parents of these children.

At the other end of the chronological scale we hear of middle-aged or elderly people being refused NHS surgery based on age, rather than on need or appropriateness. Of course if socialising has been inappropriate most of a lifetime, it might be harder for that patient to adapt and 'pass', as they would wish. The anguish she feels may mean that all of a lifetime, instead of most of it, might have been spent in a limbo of pain and compromise.

Being older does however mean there is more probable problems on medical grounds, with slower healing, difficulties in anaesthesia and postoperative prognosis.

Compassion, it seems, has a date stamp and the 'use by' date seems to apply to far too many areas of health care. Surely it should not be "too late" to help anybody or take them seriously, if you can estimate several years of happy life expectancy against a painful decline in the wrong body or gender?

39.   Who Do We Blame?

Perhaps nobody can clearly show why gender dysphoria occurs, but it is clear nobody can be blamed for it, unless it is "dodgy water" (Oestrogenic - female hormones and various chemical contaminants) and polluted foodstuffs.

It is not a parent's fault, nor is it the sufferer's.

Nobody would choose to be unhappy or dysphoric.

We can be permitted to ascribe blame to the poor services that exist to assist trans people; they should be assessed and criticised. Why are the elements of care so poorly resourced?

I guess because it is an unglamorous area of Medicine and Psychiatry, a minority interest.

We can see that a great deal needs to be done to improve standards of the care available. Simply monitoring a problem and creating hoops for patients to crawl through, relying on a large portion of sufferers to take things into their own hands and "go private" perhaps inappropriately, or toddle off this mortal globe, is not achieving what the Harry Benjamin Standards were set up to achieve.

Part of the blame for this deplorable state of affairs in treatments in the British Isles can perhaps be placed in a system which has created the minds of the men who lead our government, social, ecclesiastical, legal and medical systems in a somewhat Victorian, patriarchal and fearful way. By this I mean that the idea of difference (a female principle) causes consternation, involves changing attitudes and moving towards the twenty-first century as we in fact move beyond the millennium.

If we ask why another post-imperial power, the Netherlands, and other European Nations, seem to have made more progress in these matters, perhaps the answer is that liberalisation and humanism has meant that the need to address the needs of minorities (including a majority - women) have been largely met. Trans are a forgotten minority, only just emerging from obscurity and persecution. I believe that if women had a more prominent input into medicine and the Law, we would effect a transformation in how the needs of these minorities are met.

40. So what do I mean by Difference and the Existential?

If you are 'different' you can either hide it or accept who you are. You need to accept yourself in an existential way. You do not need to shout it from rooftops, outing yourself, but you need to know that you are OK. It is better to say of yourself "I'm OK" rather than "I'm a monster!"

As Chambers Dictionary defines existentialism as *"A term covering a number of related doctrines, denying objective universal values and holding that a person must create values for himself (herself) through action and by living each moment to the full."*

The Existential movement as described by Heidigger in 1967 is a philosophy which concentrates on *understanding existence* in contrast to the earlier Cartesian preoccupation with thinking, on *being rather than knowing*. It suggests *sum ergo cogito* I am therefore I think, instead of *cogito ergo sum*.

Sartre places stoicism in the face of anxiety and despair. Laing (1960) places awareness of the self and others before consideration of the unconscious process.

Carl Rogers in his book *On Becoming a Person, a Therapist's View of Psychotherapy*, in his chapter entitled *A Therapists View of the Good Life*, describes what he calls the characteristics of the process in which he talks of an *"Increasing Openness to Experience"* as the polar opposite of defensiveness.

If a person could be fully open to his experience, every experience, and every stimulus - whether originating within the organism or in the environment - this would be freely relayed through the nervous system without being distorted by any defensive mechanism ...

The 'good life' appears to be a movement away from the pole of defensiveness towards the pole of openness to experience. This involves an increasing tendency to live fully in each moment ... the self and personality emerge from experience.

I suggest that this sense of freedom, touched nervously on by Sartre in his book "Intimacy" is both liberating and frightening. If taken up as a way of being, the shackles of society's view, or by self-stereotyping, can be abandoned and an individual can emerge.What sort of person can one be?

A Lacota Sioux friend of mine, NapeWasteWin suggests a good dictum: *"Be the best version of yourself you can be"*.

A half-life self stifled or crushed by stereotyping into the oppression of labels and self-doubt is no life at all. Suicide is not a good option. Be yourself, not who you are told you 'should be'. It is better to exist than to exit.

I maintain that diversity is a normal aspect of nature and difference must be respected, but need not divide us. As individuals our thoughts can inspire or crush us, as can the words and actions of others.

Society has for far too long been reinforced by outmoded and unjust laws, which have marginalized, stigmatised, even penalised the T person.

It is time to walk tall! Each of us who is 'different' in any way need not be harmed by others, or by ourselves. Identity seems to be made up of inherent characteristics upon which life superimposes further layers. One can choose to live as the person one is, if no harm is done to others. Living in the light of day, with windows open and curtains drawn apart, or to live behind shutters, with windows closed, to live a restricted and often secret life. This cannot be healthy.

Life is not a dream, nor should it be a nightmare or a prison.

41.   Recommendations on the Level of Care.

I do not like the word "should", however in order that there are reasonable levels of care, I would hope that:

1.   Both the Health Service and the Private Sectors of Care adopt the philosophy as well as the guidelines of the New SOC, and that they are not simply paid lip service.

2. Flexibility. Clinicians need to see patients as individuals by treating them as such, holistically, instead of simply by the book, or worse arbitrarily.

3. The position of intersexed children and of adult hermaphrodites needs to be clarified.

4. Treating the Individual. A greater person-centred therapeutic effort should be put into the type of care available.

5. Inputs by trained, experienced, Counsellors and Psychotherapists be included in the care plan to enable a client to resolve personal issues and dilemmas during, and for a time after, the process of GRS.

6. A team approach, which more includes, the patient, Psychiatrists, Surgeon, Endocrinologist, Counsellor, Speech therapist, G.P. and other specialists would be advantageous. This would be better if only in terms of good communication and respect between the experts, including the client.

7. Labels and stereotypes need to be avoided where possible.

8. Options should be explained and explored. Those who do not seek surgery but wish to live in-role, those seeking to live as androgynes, and those who are Transvestites may need help in coming to terms with who they are.

9. There seems to be little help for partners, parents or children of transexed, transgendered, or transvestite people.

10. Research, follow-up and auditing should be included as part of the SOC. I believe that clients would be willing to assist with research, if follow-up work is seen to be part of their assessment and treatment and a condition of their acceptance for help by a G.I.C.

11. The G.I.C.'s need to employ researchers who do not work in isolation, but as part of the HBIGDA international team, using standardised methodologies and decent sized research samples. Only when effective auditing demonstrates the advantages of treatment will we avoid Health Authorities deprioritising GRS as "Cosmetic".

12. Professionals should avoid Sexism and Ageism in any care plan. Whilst it is clear practical cautions need to be applied both ends of the chronological scale, should we in fact adopt tacit policies, which exclude a patient because she is elderly?

13. Self-help groups: GIC's would do well in the U.K. if they co-operated with the various self-help groups, (providing funding, providing venues, giving inputs) to encourage group meetings, training sessions, seminars, and conferences in regional centres on a regular basis. This might provide a sense of belonging and involvement, which could dispel some of the mutual suspicion, which seems to exist between Psychiatrists in particular and their patients. To get the best from a group session I do not believe that the psychiatrist making the decisions involving care should facilitate these sessions or use them as a replacement for one-to-one work.

14. Funding. This should be national, with regional centres of excellence.

15. Waiting Lists must not be allowed to compromise a patient's standard of care by doubling and tripling the length of the Life Test. If there is impeccable evidence that the Life test has been fulfilled before presentation to a GIC, why can this not be taken as completed by a particular patient?

16. Law. As long as there are legal anomalies it is important that professionals work towards changes in the law to make full assimilation into the actual gender in Society recognised by the law. I see this as part of the process.

In my thirty-eight years trying to help in this community and more recently in my counselling practice, it has been easy to see the problem themes. Almost always there is low self-esteem, depression and guilt. These are widespread among people who are often gifted survivors both of an inadequate system of care and of an accident of nature, which has had repercussions as great as any illness, not simply for themselves, but for those around them.

42. There is a Problem in Treating Identity by Medical Means.

Gender Dysphoria is a natural variation as I keep stressing. It should be de-medicalised like homosexuality. It is different to being gay because medical interventions are needed to resolve it. Medications (hormones), psychiatry (assessment) and surgery may be involved, so there must be diagnosis for treatment to take place. It is a specialised area of Science, involving endocrinologists, geneticists, speech therapists and other treatments as well as the social interventions required to resolve things. It is not a mental illness, but suffering it many do get depressed or show other symptoms. The Health Service is able to help and a doctor should monitor the patient's blood pressure and other problems.

But there are traditional dynamics between practitioners and their patients - the omniscient doctor and the respectful sick person, who is at a disadvantage in seeking this help. This has been particularly true of those seeking help suffering with gender dysphoria. GD is not an illness, but rather is a problem of identity, which in the case of the transexed person often requires medical and/or surgical intervention to resolve.

There need to be Standards of Care which are inclusive of the informed client, not simply Standards designed to protect the doctors and surgeons from malpractice suits brought by hostile colleagues or disgruntled patients. At present these Standards appear to work with the mindset that there is such a thing as a standard person. There is not. Let alone a standard T person. The human mind is complex. A sense of identity incorporates a sense of gender, which surely needs to be congruent with that person's mind.

Of course nobody can live life as a fantasy, but if a person's gender is incongruent with his or her body they need medical and surgical help to fully live the life they aspire to. There is no litmus test for "True Transsexuality" any more than there is a standard man or woman. There can only be averages. Average does not mean the same as normal and normal does not necessarily mean acceptable or good. Famine, poverty, pain, cancer, ageing and death are all realities, all normal, but are they inevitable, desirable?

Should we not strive for change and improvement in our society? Of course we are still stuck with death, but in the 21st century quality of life and respect are achievable.

43.   No Person should be Forced to Live a Lie,

pretending to have a gender identity they do not have. That is like requiring a heterosexual to live as a gay person. It is not so long ago in the "good old days of eugenics" that doctors tried to cure their gay patients and later transsexuals. These so-called deviant people were given electric shock treatment, aversion therapy, lobotomies, drugs and other invasive methods to make them "NORMAL".

That approach is now seen as barbaric, primitive, lacking respect, and furthermore, it did not work.

Still the mythology that "doctor is always right" persists. There is often a failure of communication and of trust both ways, which gets in the way of truth and appropriate person-based treatments. The transactional dynamic between doctor and client is often that of a "stern parent" doctor opposing the "naughty child" patient. This makes it hard for a clinician to reach the truth and provide appropriate help for the client.

Instead of directing Care Standards to an individual holistically, the person is required to fit certain standards before they will be helped.

A conspiracy of pretence has grown, whereby applicants for hormonal or surgical interventions tell the G.I.C psychiatrists what they know or believe they want to hear. It becomes a script, so that they will get hormones and treatment for transsexualism, irrespective of that client's actual gender identity. As these clients lie, the G.I.C. psychiatrists become less willing to sort out the truth and see if they can help.

The truth is often lost. Mistakes can be made. The gatekeeper approach of some patriarchal psychiatrists often means that the client is excluded from appropriate help if they actually do speak the truth. All too often in the past a client will have lied to the professionals, or themselves.

It was not unusual for a professional to approach these problems with an attitude of "this is what you need", instead of giving the time to actually help a client. The psychotherapeutic benefit is lost if they act as gatekeepers, rather than as facilitators.

Certainly more listening (both ways), more consultation, more taking personal responsibility by the client, and a reality of inclusion in the treatment protocols will help.

There is some considerable way to go before this group of people feel properly served by the NHS and some of the more exploitative sections of the private sector and other support services.

The client may be so confused as to not know the truth, and will need counselling therapies to discover who they really are and to come to terms with this. It is true that what one wants may not be what one needs; but equally how can a clinician who is exposed to a text rather than the truth judge that the help given or refused is appropriate? Appointments are too brief, too few and far between. The largest G.I.C.'s have too many seeking help and are under-resourced.

44. Care Standards as Opposed to Standards of Care.

Standards of Care should be high as standards and clear and flexible as protocols, in all areas of psychiatry and medicine. They should not be used other than as Guidelines. Nor should they be used by gatekeeper-psychiatrists to exclude those who are distressed, or who do not fit a particular pattern or theory, or view of what a man or a woman 'should be' from treatment protocols.

Humans are not totally gender bipolar. We all share masculine and feminine aspects in our personalities and characters.

Trans people present, seeking medical or surgical assistance in reaching a personal gender harmony or euphoria, as opposed to being forced to pretend to be someone they are not, or rejected and excluded from any help.

The Standards of Care (SOC) remain in the balance. This has not been helped by the incomplete acceptance of transition in legal terms until 2004. This failure to change the role of Birth Certificates as identity documents has resulted in stigmatisation of an already vulnerable group of people.

We never again should hear that someone has been persecuted for being himself or herself.

- T People are open to prosecution for using public toilets if a complaint is made.
- Adoption, parental and access rights are not assured.
- State Pensionable ages are still fixed to the NI number in their records which indicates retirement ages as different for men (65) and women (60) for those who might wish to retire at 60 over the next few years. The Gerbil/Act has addressed some of the Pension issues, but problems still exist.

More information from the Department for Constitutional Affairs *http://www.dca.gov.uk/constitution/transsex/*

- The CRB procedures potentially endanger people's privacy and there is a need to challenge this. Applying for Criminal Records clearance, if you teach, are a nurse, carer etc needs to be approached carefully.
(See the Press for Change website *http://www.pfc.org.uk/*)
- Harassment still occurs in some areas and is not yet properly prosecuted by the law. Local Police Authorities are still evolving standards and policies to protect minorities, GLBT (= Gay, lesbian, Bisexual, Trans) Rights are real. Complain if there is a problem from another person or especially from the police or other officials.
- Treatment of TS conditions varies from area to area.
- The press seems to be able to ridicule sensationalise and belittle the T community without the Press Council taking any action against them.

This will all have to change if challenged in law. The Government Consultative Body had to take this ruling into account in their findings and Report for the Gerbil (Gender Recognition Bill now Act).

45. There are still Failures in Care and Casualties of the Treatments Available.

One of the first principals of Medicine is "Do no harm". When providing any treatment, which is irreversible, both client and clinician need certainty. To find this, they need truth, trust, time and an attitude of mutual respect.

There was a Conference presented at the Royal Society of Medicine on April 16th 2002 in London on *"Gender Identity Disorder in Adults - Guidance for the Management of Transsexualism - Towards a Uniform Treatment Approach"*.

Standards were suggested that caused such a furore since they lacked any inclusion for a proposed National Consultation process regarding the controversial Standards of Care.

It resulted in considerable discussion and work with support groups and individual people to try to get these Standards right. There was a real problem with the proposed SOC, which were presented by Dr. Brian Ferguson. There was a peaceful demonstration outside and people from all the significant T support organisations attended and had a lot to say. Sadly it ended with no firm agreement for consultation to take place, but hopefully these standards will be dropped. I gained the impression that Dr. Ferguson and the organisers felt out of their depth, when faced with the reaction of T people and many of the professionals in this field.

There was a volume of largely constructive criticism from the client group. Patient Power and awareness challenged the medic's assumptions and lack of good practice, which seemed to have excluded the client from the team. This approach is contrary to that which the modern Health Service is supposed to provide. The feelings and erudition of those requesting, or insisting, quite reasonably, that they have the same right to consultation as any group requiring NHS help, simply terminated any public discussion of the actual issues in question.

The Royal College of Nurses also mounted a Conference in May that year, about Trans people in Nursing and Nursing T people.

COUNSELLING GENDER DYSPHORIC CLIENTS:

46. Gender Counselling and its Difficulties in Cases of Acute and Chronic G.D.

My experience with gender dysphoric sufferers commenced many years ago. My aim was to help people in chronic or acute crisis, situations that were challenged by their belief that they might be transexed. Questions concerning their gender identity, their core personality consumed many of my clients.

The client tended to regard me as the expert, the person with authority. The initial transferences largely worked with the counsellor as the expert in this way (Berne on transactional therapy). Because clients wanted to be 'told what to do', there could be a great temptation to be overly directive or pragmatic. Caution was the name of the game.

Options were always, so far as possible, highlighted for the client, so that he or she could make important choices. They were helped with cognitive problem solving techniques and provided, as far as possible in advance, with all the information possible. Ignorance has always been a problem with not only the clients, but also many professionals.

The numbers of distressed persons coming to me was so great because the GIC's rarely provided any counselling. The NHS faces large numbers of clients whose needs were not, in most senses, being met by the Gender Identity Clinics or by other professionals who were either ignorant of this field or hostile to it.

General practitioners, local psychiatrists and psychologists were not addressing this problem. Almost no counselling which was geared for the particular difficulties of clients with gender identity difficulties, was available on the N.H.S.

Sessions had to be limited in number because of limited resources. They included a preliminary history and assessment prior to counselling, and a clear contract to address a particular difficulty. Also we provided clients with information, so that they could make informed decisions.

The counselling provided had to be a form of crisis management, with brief counselling support, backed up with peer group support, information and advice in other contexts (conferences, information provision, workshops and seminars, involving inputs from myself and other professionals in the field).

I worked from a multidisciplinary theoretical base, using specialised knowledge derived from Harry Benjamin, Stoller, Green and Money, Freud, Jung, Ellis, Hirschfeld and others.

Much of the work was undertaken with a clear contract to address particular issues, using Windy Dryden's Rational Emotive Therapy as the main model. This involves using an eclectic, largely cognitive, approach to bring about change, based on the hypothesis that humans have a tendency towards irrationality; but, optimistically, that we also have a great potential to work to change our biologically based irrationalities.

By identifying goals, setting a contract to address a particular difficulty and actively pursuing these goals, using a cognitive approach to reach these insights, therapy enables a client to change.

The B.A.C. Code of Ethics was applied, as were The Standards of Care in Treatment of Transsexuals. Counselling was often in my home or the client's, since no premises was available owing to lack of funding and to keep costs as low as possible to the client. Sessions were from one to two hours (two in cases where long distance travel had been involved).

Client's difficulties and themes, which have recurred, are:

1. Clarification, helping the client to clarify whether he/she is genuinely gender dysphoric; or, for example, a guilty transvestite convincing himself he is transexed to escape that guilt.
2. Motivation. The client who sees himself as a failed man and (foolishly) believed that life as a woman is easier.
3. Poor self-esteem and Self-hate.
4. Poor ego development.
5. Self restriction, Unrealistic views about what a woman or a man are 'supposed to be', a self imposed stereotypicality.
6. Inferiority,

   Being a little man with no penis (in the case of the FtM's).

   Being an unconvincing woman in the case of many MtF's because of an 'inappropriate' education and life history.
7. Practicality,

   Not passing as a member of the gender role chosen (in the case of some of the MtF's).
8. Guilt. Because of family disruption or religious difficulties.
9. Divorce and the effect on children and partners.
10. Relationships. Sexuality, friendships, partners, parents etc.
11. Loneliness and isolation.
12. Employment and Housing.
13. Unrealistic expectations of surgery and post operative complications; surgery junkies.
14. Medication, including hormones induced mood swings.
15. Depression and thoughts of suicide.
16. Alcoholism, drug abuse.
17. Bereavement.

    (Mourning a past life, and to an extent adjusting to the negative implications of Surgery.
18. Lost fertility, lost libido etc.) and a plethora of other difficulties.

It left me as a counsellor with a feeling rather like the little Dutch girl with her finger in the dyke, or was it a boy?

The politics of the last forty years have been rather like the earlier attitude of many professionals to homosexuals. The professional's script

85

has been to somehow 'cure' the person and to "make him/her 'normal'."

Often the attitude of professionals has been very far removed from the humanistic core conditions of Carl Rogers with his use of empathy warmth and genuineness. Ignorance or prejudice was rife. There were also self-styled counsellors who did actual damage to clients by telling clients what to do instead of listening.

I encouraged clients to participate in the process by working at home, as well as in the consultation room, with reading lists and homework and self-appraisals. Much of my work was intuitive and based on experience with these clients, working around evidence and clues in a diagnostic sense, to some extent looking at practical realities. It was largely successful, but felt a bit like triage at a battle front.

I was attracted to Rogers's "Way of being" with a client. Though I knew my theoretical background and practice had not harmed a client and had helped many. I reacted against the very directive self-styled 'counsellors' who were actually harming their clients, many of whom had subsequently come to us for help.

47. TWO ATYPICAL CLIENTS

To illustrate the problems faced by two very different 'transexed' people and the range of counselling skills required I describe the experience of two of my clients.

Most Trans people have issues arising alongside the gender thing. Some of these are illustrated in the Surveys I present later in this book.

Obviously I protect Client's confidentiality.

I worked for a local Area Health Authority Dept of Psychology/ Counselling.

In "Client 2", I describe briefly the long term Process of Personal Counselling, for the benefit of those interested in counselling in this context.

CLIENT 1.

I recall a client who had attended a Gender Identity Clinic and had been told that he was "a transsexual" by the Consultant Psychiatrist. He was in deep depression and suicidal, and felt like a nothing. Counselling was under the supervision and in the context of the local Health Authority, in their premises.

I adopted an entirely Rogerian approach with this client, working with the process and with unlimited positive regard. I saw him on a weekly basis.

After a year he was saying that this was the first time in his life anyone had ever listened to him. This was an issue for him.

It also transpired that he was not transexed.

He was operating the mind set "If I dress as a woman sometimes, I must be one". His mother had also unmanned then mocked him, with "boys don't do that" when he had cried. There were many strong retroflexions in which he enacted his mother's problems (she seems to have had a classic Freudian penis envy).

In fact he had two fantasy personas, one a Lee Marvin type, a loner, a very masculine cowboy type; the other a Debbie Reynolds sixties girl. He would dress up as either of these and watch videos of his hero or his heroine. But they had been as he put it "at war with each other in his head" and it made him miserable. "She" was there because he rejected masculinity; 'he' was there because he felt guilty about 'her'.

He was depressed and had a very low libido and couldn't cope without his fantasy "safety valves." His long-suffering wife accepted all versions of him. He eventually accepted himself and his "eccentricity". It is a clear case where surgery would have made things very much worse.

Above all this case convinces me of the value of a client based, person centred, and empathetic approach. His defensive boundaries had been so strong he had never before admitted the facts to himself or others.

Nobody had before walked in his moccasins, or his high heels.

He did not fit the categories of diagnosis held by the N.H.S.

There seems to be an expectation that once a patient is labelled (diagnosed) they only have one dimension. His problem really seems to have been his own very rigid, sexist, view of male and female identity, with two strongly stereotypical extremes in his personality, which brought about an extreme sense of conflict and guilt about his fantasy or eccentricity, and subsequent isolation.

Using Rogers's Core conditions, in counselling him, enabled this shy person to be liberated, and he became more functional as a whole person. He was at last able to accept himself and to integrate his harmless eccentricity into his life. The therapeutic relationship we had has enabled him. He became as Rogers puts it, "a person".

Earlier work using only a cognitive approach by another counsellor had "tried to stop him dressing up", in his words, which only made him feel more guilty and suicidal.

A client presents with a problem or series of difficulties. It is the counsellor's task to help unravel the knots, to enable a client to recognise personal constructs (beliefs) which are damaging, and to be in touch with his or her feelings.

Rogers's model has demonstrated that the client is the expert. A less directive and more adult-to-adult mode of process was actually more helpful with this client than a need to 'cure' him might have been in the past. He still retains his "eccentricity", but it is not damaging him now, and his depression has gone. He is coping.

CLIENT 2.

I had one client who was genitally abused as a boy, who actually had surgery and sexual reassignment, reasoning that if the hurt member was removed it could not be hurt again.

Her presenting displacement was that she had her surgery because she was unable to bear the guilt of being a homosexual man, but that she is not a woman either because she does not have a woman's past. She was also alcoholic and a sadomasochist, and would like to abuse her abusers, other men.

This sad, intelligent, complex client has often planned her suicide, "the ultimate existential act", as she put it.

She had at times regressed, in a Freudian sense, to infantile states of mind and behaviour, and a psychodynamic Freudian approach might have, in Michael Jacobs's words "be too limited for this client".

However an Egan (person based) approach helped this client tell her story, see where her problems came from and to grieve about her mistakes. I do not know how her story will end.

I felt that this client was very much on the edge of risk of suicide or complete breakdown. I am presenting this client as her story presented particular difficulties for me:

The client was suicidal and had severe identity problems, describing herself as an "it". She was profoundly depressed, but she was an adrenaline addict, as she says, "turned on by power" and enjoys as she puts it "A losers fight". I feared that she saw counselling as a means to endorse her own negative feelings about herself, rather than as a means to learn to accept and cope with her life. The more pain and anger she revealed the more determined to kill herself she seemed to be.

I asked colleagues in supervision what I might do to facilitate such a negative client, other than what I was already able to do with my own limited resources. I referred her for psychiatry at Charing Cross Hospital, where they did offer her a once a month group session. The effect was hopeless since the facilitator was also the gate-keeping psychiatrist. Her needs were more immediate than that. Talking in the tea-room to "other Trannies" as she put it, did help her a bit.

The client had referred herself to me for counselling after a friend persuaded her that she needed help.

PRESENTING PROBLEM:

This client, who I will call Pat, presented with extreme identity dysfunction. She used phrases like "I don't know who I am any more". She was suicidal because a feminist friend had told her she could never be a real woman that she was in fact a homosexual man who had had surgery to escape from her childhood abuser. She tended to agree with her friend's assessment of herself, and certainly came over as rather like a verbally challenging and aggressive political man, rather than as a stereotypical female.

She said, "transsexualism gets in the way of everything I do". She was against stereotypes (as I am), but used labels and pseudo-rationalisations as rods to beat herself with, rather than exploring her feelings, taking personal responsibility or learning to define herself as a real individual with any sort of future.

Feelings were so very painful for her.

She had been off sick from work (because of stress) for several months. She had been drinking over a bottle of vodka a night and was very deeply in debt.

INITIAL ASSESSMENT AND HISTORY

I worked over seven one hourly sessions with this client.

She made some real progress and had reached a fairly positive and rational stage in her process over the first five sessions and at the sixth was very blocked about where her rage might be placed.

We agreed at the end of her sixth session that she would write her feelings as a letter to her abuser, who seemed to have a lot to do with her self-hate. Instead she wrote a letter to her parents who she saw as to blame for all the mistakes she had made in her life. At the last session she provided this letter to her now deceased parents.

This client seemed to be drowning in self-doubt, guilt and self-hate. She has transferred all the blame to her parents, now dead.

She had at first meeting, the resolve and the means and will to commit suicide. This resolve was expressed at each session.

She had recently decided to give herself a gender-neutral name rather than the female one she had adopted before her surgery. It was because she said she was in fact an "it".

CONTRACT WITH THIS CLIENT:

This client was at severe risk. She knew all the helping agencies and felt none could help her (Samaritans, the N.H.S.)

Each counselling session acted "as a focus of hope" she said, but her dilemmas became more focused as she worked through her difficulties.

At the end of each session we made a contract for the next session with an element of "homework", where she resolved before the next session to do the following:

1. Describe herself as she sees herself ..."good" and "bad points"
2. Describe herself as she imagines others see her.
3. Write the unsent letter to her abuser.
4. Attend a group at Charring Cross Hospital.
5. See the surgeon to seek a realistic appraisal of her body image
6. Contact her daughters, two actually had been seeking resumption of contact with her and needed her help and advice.

We met one-to-one for hourly sessions. She always was punctual. Counselling was on neutral territory, away from a hospital environment.

HISTORY AND CONTENT OF PREVIOUS SESSIONS:

My client was 54 years old at the time of these sessions.

I refer to the client as "she", in the post-operative phase of her life, and "he" prior to that. As a boy Pat had been grossly abused by an older boy over several years, abuse which involved inflicting pain on his genitals, anal sex and beatings. But the abuser "took notice of" Pat. She says she is herself sadomasochistic.

At boarding school this working class boy was also involved both as victim then as abuser of other boys. Pat grew to hate his genitals, had developed transvestite tendencies and rationalised that as a woman he might not be so abused. This was seen as killing the male aggressive thing he so hated. There also seemed to be a strongly masochistic element in this.

There was not much sign of an innate feminine or female nature, if by this we mean gentleness or nurturing. Although she says she was "intensely jealous of women's reproductive capacity" she does not like children and took little part in their upbringing. She tended to dress in jeans and wore no make-up and actually said that she "looks like a dyke" … which I slightly resented as a form of her own stereotypical view of what a lesbian looks like.

Prior to sexual reassignment surgery, as a man she had married twice, had four daughters, two by each wife. The second marriage ended 16 years earlier. Three of the daughters are addictive personalities; two are drug addicts, one alcoholic. The forth has no contact with my client. Pat blames herself for all the pain she has inflicted on both "unsuspecting wives and all the children".

Sexual preference was for males. Both the marriages were, Pat says, a denial of his strong homosexual drive, where he "colluded with his parents wishes for him to be a normal man".

This appeared to be a person who made a series of mistakes because of denial; not least defining himself as a woman because he hated being a man, and his own homophobia which has probably led him to resolve these issues in reassignment surgery.

She had sexual reassignment surgery eight years earlier. This surgery was not successful since she only had very little depth in her pseudo-vagina. I referred her for further surgery to improve this situation. She has had no sexual or caring relationships since surgery.

91

As a man Pat had worked in the transport industry. It was good money, but involved little human contact/conflict. Pat was considering returning to this type of work, but her drinking was a danger in that context.

At the time of these sessions several years ago there was a strong chance she might soon go to prison for non-payment of Community Charge ... She was very badly in debt. She was fearful that she might have been sent to a man's prison. If that happened there was no provision for postoperative transsexuals and it seemed it was up to the court whether they were sent to a male or a female prison. The birth certificate could not be amended in England so her legal status remained as a "male".

She appeared to have had her gender reassignment surgery to escape from a past of childhood sexual and physical abuse, and had many sadomasochistic traits, and felt a need to punish herself for all the "needless suffering she had inflicted on her two ex-wives and children".

She is intelligent and manipulative, and as she puts it "ruthless" (which may be how she survived this long). It may be that she wished to challenge counselling, rather than use it. She hated those who do not hate her. She "cannot bear to be loved". She seemed absorbed in maintaining her sense of personal isolation and preferred political colleagues to real friends. Emotional closeness is something she said that was too much to contemplate.

She had high walls round her inner core, which she felt was a vacuum anyway.

She presented most of her own feelings in a political context, and used the political and ethical arguments she has had hurled at her by feminist friends as sticks to beat herself with, rather than searching for her own feelings, which lay buried beneath a mass of guilt and regret. She said Society must change and allow her to be the "it" she sees herself as now.

One difficulty I had as her counsellor was that I tended to feel she has probably made a mistake in having had surgery, whilst at the same time I felt empathy for her in her own particular hell. Her problems did seem to overwhelm her, many seemed to be of her own making, but it did seem that she might do well to accept things and not be so hard on herself.

However I felt that she needed more help and time than I could give her. The N.H.S. was not resourced to provide full time help for this tragic person, until it is perhaps going to be too late. Her mode was to constantly challenge society, herself and her counsellor. I was certain that she was serious about her intention to perform what she called her "last existential act", her own suicide. This distressed me, but I do accept that this was a course she might well have chosen.

She could not cope with her feelings, and as she said "the more she feels, the less she wants to live". She often sought oblivion in alcohol abuse and described herself as an alcoholic. However, by her third session she said she did stop drinking and rejoined Alcoholics Anonymous. Drink was one of the causes of this debt.

She had great difficulty in taking responsibility for herself, because she wasn't able to do so as a child. She reached past denial and had reached her anger, but had not come to terms with her life. She might have seen me, the counsellor, as a parent figure, but she blamed her parents for allowing her abuse. This made for complex transferences and cautions in the process of counselling.

TREATMENT PLAN

This was a case where the treatment plan was to offer support by up to ten sessions, with a review at the eighth. All the resources of treatment skills, referral to other agencies, and work at home and in a group were in operation. Each session was with a particular contract, e.g. to look at her self image, at personal guilt, at her abuser, at options she sees as available to her, at her relationships with others, at how she could get by on a day to day basis etc.

We did some gestalt and some cognitive work. All sessions were none the less in an humanistic client-led mode as far as possible, although her own efforts to challenge my boundaries during sessions were an interesting variant of client leading on a couple of occasions.

SIGNIFICANT MOMENTS AND PHRASES.

Some quotes above illuminate these, but in the seventh session, when we went through her letter to her parents she said the following:

"…People like me always end up colluding in our own oppression, in real life there is never salvation, only an outcry of rage is just still feasible".

Of her marriage she said, "I remember the sheer pleasure of showing the world I was other than I am".

She said, "When I was ten the citadel of my integrity was destroyed, not once, but again and again."

She wrote in the unsent letter, "Dad, you tried to oppress me with kindness, I found kindness the least acceptable, at least you know where you are with violence and sadism".

"I crave people wanting me, but when it happens it is inevitably corrupt, there can only ever be cruelty and force".

"I can't see a way that this attempt at therapy can be other than a whinge because I can't see any option that I could have taken which would have resulted in any other course of my life."

"I was cut off from genuine human feelings by our collusion with artificial social constructs".

"I can't forgive myself for not facing up to what I now accept before it was too late."

She made progress but there was so much pain there that I felt it would take more than I could offer to get her through all this. The very fact of her being offered and accepting counselling was encouraging.

Interventions, which accessed her feelings, helped her, but she was in deep distress and in some ways her feelings were put on hold. Denial is a game she often played although she was also amazingly honest sometimes.

Gestalt work was very powerful with her. She wrote the 'unsent letter' to her now dead parents expressing her hate and anger, and eventually another to her abuser. This method of enabling a client to express repressed feelings is one I have used before and will continue to use.

Our work with dreams, and her dream diary gave her a reason "to keep coming and not to kill herself… yet" as she said. Cognitive work helped her to stop drinking, she has realised it was not a solution but a poor escape.

She sees herself as an "it" now, but at least she is less negative about that and is a "proud it" as she puts it.

This client now has chosen a gender-neutral mode of dress and name and her latest bandwagon was to become androgynous. This meant that the stress she had in maintaining a female persona, which she did not believe in, or a male one she hated, was removed. Interestingly she in no way regretted her surgery. She returned to her traditionally all-male job and largely, as she put it, escaped from the tyranny of gender.

DISCUSSION

Whilst these Clients are unusual and extreme, they demonstrate that nothing is as straightforward as at first it may seem. Often there are multiple problems in cohort with the gender distress.

It is vital not to attempt to make the client fit the labels.

The majority of gender dysphoric clients appear to genuinely benefit from counselling, even on a brief counselling basis. Once the core identity issue is addressed many of the other difficulties seem to be less distressing and depressing. Gender distress seems to be at its most acute at times of choice. "What am I?" as well as "Who am I?" is the question.

Once identity is established, then the issue becomes "how shall I live my life". The counsellor's task is to enable the client to deal with his or her own decisions and the consequences of these decisions.

It sometimes feels like an almost impossible task, but it is worthwhile. What we need is resources and trained people to develop the work.

48.   The So-called "Real Life Test" and Employment.

If you are in a Union they often have Policies and will help negotiate your employment situation if you need this. Sometimes it is better to be a student during "Transition". Students often can look a bit androgynous anyway and Universities and the National Union of Students can be helpful.

If you are self employed you will need to demonstrate that you function successfully as your gender in a context where you meet other people. You should not hide away pretending that you are dealing with this experience. It will not help you deal with life after surgery; people see and meet you, not usually your genitals.

As a pre-operative TS you are expected by your Gender Identity Clinic to be in stable employment in your new gender role for a considerable time, at least a year, before you might be put on the waiting list for surgery. This means that you are not only beset with an inappropriate birth certificate (and curriculum vitae), but that your body, and often appearance, still does not accord with your own, or your employer's, expectations.

With equal opportunity regulations, that should not be an employment difficulty. But of course there is. If you remain with the same employer (e.g. British Telecom is very good) you may be relocated and greatly helped. Unions have in some cases negotiated on behalf of employees to enable this transition to take place painlessly. With smaller companies it may not be so easy.

For those who meet the public face to face there can be problems. Work-mates and colleagues may not mind how you dress - they may find it amusing, intriguing, confusing, sad or annoying. But what is almost certain, in our anally retentive society, is that someone may complain of, or be concerned about, which loo should s(he) use?

Dressed as a female you can't go to the gents - but whilst still physically equipped as a male it is 'not right' that you should go to the ladies. Nobody can work all day with their legs crossed!

In these delicate matters a TS person certainly should not leave the seat up if she's stood to micturate (pee I mean), but why is she standing anyway? I know ... it's the state of some loos ... men do have sensible plumbing in that respect! This may sound funny but apparently there are TS's who do this sort of irritatingly stupid thing. Women are amazed by men's poor aim in the loo - and the seat always being up is annoying - if that happens in the lady's loo it's too much!

Many TS's realise only too late that if they have changed over from being a 'male' engineer to being, say a secretary, the rates of pay for traditionally 'female' jobs are much lower than those for 'male' ones. Even in unskilled work, a labourer earns much more than a shop-girl, or a nurse. There are therefore major pitfalls in economic terms. If you are lucky and have a profession you may find you can change and carry on, though I gather it is not easy, for example, in teaching.

Perhaps retraining, or a return to college is a good idea. If you cannot get paid work in your new mode then do voluntary work as a woman or a man for Red Cross, Help the Aged or something like that, while you sign on.

There is absolutely nothing to gain by staying at home - not learning to integrate socially - save of course personal safety! If you cannot function socially in your new role, then how could you fully benefit by having surgery, which is intended to improve your lifestyle? The idea of perception of gender as a two way dynamic - and a good life as not being that of a solitary - is commonplace. It also involves a little of the 'you should' judgmentalism.

It is interesting that there is an implicit suggestion, perceived by the client group, in the Standards of Care, that a transexed person needs to conform with the world's view of what a woman or man 'should be'. They must 'pass' - and perhaps not enough attention is paid to her, or his, own need to be at peace with herself, or himself. But life is a hard judge and a pragmatic approach is sometimes wise - or adoption of a very thick skin.

This 'real life test' has evolved to avoid providing hormones or surgery for the patient who has never been in public in the opposite role, who changes clothes in the hospital loo, before presenting to the team at a GIC, and who may well later regret having had 'inappropriate' surgery.

Some critics complain that this is a paternalistic view of the GD client, as a person who will lie, and is unable to make an informed choice - it keeps the patient in her place.

The opposing view would be that if a patient is daft enough to elect to have inappropriate surgery, it is his responsibility - but it is also the surgeon or psychiatrist who will be sued. Later, perhaps, the GIC would have pleas for corrective reconstruction surgery to change back, or there might be suicides of these sad individuals. However, I wonder how many suicides there are during this particularly fraught time for this group anyway?

The requirement that a patient must be employed and thus demonstrate his or her stability to the GIC shows them that s(he) is sincere and might be successful in the change over - so it is probably appropriate.

There is a catch 22 - if you can't get a job before surgery - you probably can't have surgery until you have worked. A little constructive help with CV's and a plan of getting into employment - with a decent reference may help save some very difficult times ahead.

The Sex Discrimination Act 1975 outlaws discrimination on the ground of sex in the sphere of employment, provision of goods and services, accommodation and education. Both men and women can make claims. However 'sex' signifies original sex (biologically) not present gender or sexual orientation. (Discrimination against homosexuals and gay people, as such, is not unlawful under the Act.)

The law is a mess on employment, although recent legislation has improved things considerably. Even if you do your job well - if you can get one - you may be caught out and lose it. You have to be better than good to be average - as do most women in 'male' jobs. Good luck.

Whether we like it or not, the 'historical document', the Birth Certificate, can cause great problems throughout one's life. Perhaps one solution is to be self-employed. At least you know your references are good (or bad). To be serious, it is matter of considerable concern that the TS is in a worse position than most 'disabled' persons in the job market and there is generally little or no sympathy from an employer who has been lied to, or told the truth - another catch 22.

Employment legislation (like Unfair dismissal) is hard to evoke in defence of the TS situation. Some unions have good records and so do some employers. Others, not so. If you have had a skill as a 'man' or 'woman' before surgery it need not be rejected out of hand. More and more men and women are crossing the stereotype wall, to do jobs usually done traditionally by one sex or the other. Avoid publicity - employers don't like that.

49. The Standards of Care (SOC) for Hormonal and Surgical Reassignment of G.D. Persons.

As of the beginning of 1979, an undocumented estimate of the number of adult Americans hormonally and surgically sex reassigned ranged from 3,000 to 6,000. Also undocumented is the estimate that between 30,000 and 60,000 USA citizens consider themselves to be valid candidates for sex reassignment.

World estimates are not available. As of mid-1978, approximately 40 centres in the Western hemisphere offered surgical sex reassignment to persons having a multiplicity of behavioural diagnoses applied under a multiplicity of criteria.

In recent decades, the demand for sex reassignment has increased, as have the number and variety of possible psychological, hormonal and surgical treatments. The rationales upon which such treatments are offered have become more and more complex. Varied philosophies of appropriate care have been suggested by various professionals, identified as experts, on the topic of gender identity.

However, until the present, no statement of the standard of care to be offered to gender dysphoric patients (sex reassignment applicants) has received official sanction by any identifiable professional group. The present document is designed to fill that void.

Copies of the Standards of Care may be obtained via a link from the GENDYS Network Website. It is this author's view that the situation regarding care, evaluation and follow up is very far from these minimal criteria in the United Kingdom. Even so there are professionals who are struggling against underfunding, overwork and even unsympathetic colleagues, who attempt to approach a proper ethical and effective caring and scientific approach to those who genuinely suffer from gender dysphoria.

Those patients with funds who 'go private', sometimes it seems are able to get rapid, almost on demand, hormonal and surgical intervention. This is sadly often without regard to the suitability of the patient, or the Standards of Care that one might expect, or at least hope for.

Those who are National Health patients receive varying standards of care, and have dreadful waiting lists to deter them. Little of the care which is available even begins to match up to the standards of care propounded by the Harry Benjamin International Gender Dysphoria Association.

The transexed person deserves good standards of care and has rights - the same rights as all citizens. These standards both protect the practitioner and specify proper standards, which a patient might expect.

The SOC in the UK are being reviewed since those proposed by the HBIGDA are considered best suited to the United States, which are more litigious than in the UK.

Let us hope they consider these points ... and those mentioned in Recommendations (section 41)

50.   Gender Identity Clinics (GIC's) - Charing Cross Hospital.

On the following pages is a copy of the policy document of Europe's largest Gender Identity Clinic at Charing Cross Hospital in London, was kindly provided by Dr. Don Montgomery. This unit was started by the (notorious to some) late Dr. John Randall in the mid-sixties.

Work is also being done at the Portman Clinic in London for adolescent transexed children and their families. Help is available for adults at smaller sub-units around the UK.

All large hospitals come up against the problems of transgendered people. As a casualty sister, this author was well aware of this, and the lack of provision for the confusion this can cause. A woman presenting with a prostate problem or a man with no penis can be confusing.

There are various Departments of Psychiatry around the country which take an interest in the plight of the Gender Dysphoric person, but this depends on local consultants being interested in this subject. The concept of a GIC suggests proper funding with reasonable resources and like all NHS units is under great financial restraints, and overload, with funding and bureaucratic problems and over long waiting lists.

They are trying to arrange a compromise between what is possible, what is practical and what can be afforded. Sadly medical and surgical science is an expensive and limited resource.

Usually a patient is referred by his/her GP to a psychiatrist before any treatment commences. Other agencies do recommend a range of possible help available. The GENDYS Network hopes to provide update lists on what is happening around the UK.

The Standards of Care (HBIGDA) acted as a broad guide for psychiatrists, endocrinologists, psychologists and surgeons. A multi-disciplined approach is an ideal, with a co-ordinated holistic (whole view) of the patient.

A broad rule of thumb is that the patient should ideally be:

1. Single in civil law (ideally)
2. Over 18 (sometimes taken as over 21 - or very close co-operation with parents and the child is required, if under 18)
3. Hormones are only administered if it is safe medically.
4. Before being put on the waiting list for surgery the patient should live and work and function socially in the role of adoption.

5. The patient should ideally present in a reasonably convincing mode, and form satisfactory crucial interactions with others and be accepted by others in the world at large, in the role of adoption.

The 1995 Policy
Riverside Mental Health Trust, Gender Identity Clinic

Charing Cross Hospital, Fulham Palace Road, London W6 8RF
Gender Reassignment - Charing Cross Hospital
Clinical Management Policy July 1995

The Standards of Care promulgated by the Harry Benjamin International Gender Dysphoria Association Inc. act as guidelines to clinicians working in the field of gender identity disorders throughout the world, although some clinicians modify these criteria and some even seem to ignore them.

The Gender Identity Clinic at Charing Cross Hospital uses these Standards of Care as firm and ethical guidelines to a great extent.

A typical patient referred to this Clinic by a general practitioner, psychiatrist or other relevant clinician, might follow the following pathway:

1. An initial consultation with a psychiatrist.

2. A second opinion consultation with a different psychiatrist or psychologist.

3. A follow-up appointment with either of the above, who would take over the Psychiatric assessment and counselling of the patient. Follow-up appointments might be somewhere between three and six months apart.

4. Psychologically and geographically available patients might be referred to a monthly group psychotherapy programme.

5. After a suitable period of counselling and probably a further opinion from the alternative clinician initially involved in the assessment process the patient might be recommended for contra-sex hormone therapy. Such a recommendation could come somewhere between three months and five years of attendance at our clinic.

6. Either before referral to our clinic or during the process of assessment and counselling described above the patient might make a decision to continue in their transsexual ambitions and to begin to

101

live in the opposite gender role. There are no particular gateway criteria for the patient making this decision, although they would have hopefully been counselled in a relevant manner prior to such a step.

7. The patient then attempts to fulfill a valid 'Real Life Test' living full time in the chosen gender role. The patient would need to demonstrate acceptance by society in this role and improved social and psychological functioning. For one year of this two-year period the patient would need to demonstrate acceptance and integration in society by being financially independent in employment, or involved in full time education or training. For some patients of limited psychological or social resources or in place of very high unemployment our clinic might accept evidence of significant employment in the voluntary sector.

8. After the managing clinician feels the patient has fulfilled a valid 'Real Life Test' the patient would then have a further consultation with another clinician to obtain a supportive second opinion prior to referral to the clinic surgeon. The clinic surgeon would make his own judgement as to whether to offer the patient surgery or not, and of course this criteria for acceptance would include whether the physical health of the patient could warrant major surgery.

9. If previously married the patient should present evidence of divorce prior to referral to the surgeon. On some occasions couples decide to stay legally married adopting a 'sisterly' relationship. In that case a legal affidavit from the wife regarding her understanding of the nature of the surgery and permission for such an operation needs to be obtained.

10. From the surgical aspect all the above is necessary, and after being seen by the surgeon and if suitable and agreeable, the patient's name is placed on the surgical waiting list. After this it is essential that the patient attend the psychiatric outpatient clinic to maintain regular contact for ongoing assessment until their names reach the top of the waiting list and they are sent for.

The waiting list can be approximately two years and this period of ongoing assessment while on the waiting list is of important value to the patient and the supervising clinicians.

Ref: Standards of Care: The Hormonal and Surgical Sex Reassignment of Gender Dysphoric Persons (Harry Benjamin International Gender Dysphoria Association Inc). Walker P., Berger J., et al. Archives of Sexual Behaviour 1985. 14:79-90.

By now the reader will be aware of the difficulties of proving the aetiology and treatment of transsexualism. This applies to many of the chronic conditions for which medicine provides treatment. The complexity of scientific and social theories, and their inter-relationship, makes it clear that the precise cause of transsexualism is unknown and possibly will never be fully understood. Health Service policy and the function of therapy is theoretically increasingly moving towards the promotion of an improved quality of life, rather than simply treatment of a precisely diagnosed condition. The measure of success should be seen in these terms rather than in the provision of a 'cure.'

Regarding items four and five above, of the so-called 'real life test' are crucially important. Those consultants who are moving away from the strict medical model to a more person-centred approach are claiming high success rates. It is important that the Real-life-test is not seen as something to please the consultant, but a test in which the person monitors him or her self.

There is a sense in which all people are undergoing a real life test. Some may feel they 'pass' this test, some fail. Will a change of role maximise or hinder progress in living life to the full? This is after all what makes a life rich and fulfilled. Seeing it as only regrets would be very depressing. Viewed in this way, the operation becomes a step, an option, or even an incidental though important factor. However, for some, life itself feels impossible without a surgical resolution.

51.   Hormones (MtF)

The 'female' hormone used in the treatment of male to female transsexuals is an Oestrogen. (Now I gather one spells Estrogen the American way - I stick to the Oestrogen spelling!)

This may be accompanied by an Androgen suppressant (testosterone suppressant).

Normally secreted in females by the ovarian follicles, some twenty-two oestrogenic substances have so far been isolated. Oestrogens belong to a class of organic chemical compounds known as steroid hormones. In women the (closely related) steroids Oestradiol, Oestrone and Oestriol are excreted in the urine. Oestradiol 17β is the most potent and is probably the oestrogen which is secreted, the others being metabolic derivatives. Like all hormones, Oestradiol is carried in the blood stream in minute amounts and acts as a catalyst on other tissues.

In the biological female, the uterus, Fallopian tubes, vagina, external genitalia and breasts develop and mature under Oestrogenic influence. Oestrogens also have effects related to gestation and lactation for which the synergistic action of progesterone, another hormone produced in the ovaries, is required. Progesterone is occasionally used in the treatment of male to female TS's, and may enhance breast development.

There is an important relationship between a person's sense of identity and the hormones to which the brain is exposed, and has been exposed to since early gestation, that is, in the months before birth. The trans woman's sense of identity as a feminine person develops and persists despite the continuous normal production of male sex hormones (androgens) throughout life, and seems to be unaffected by them.

Although in some animals evidence exists that transient exposure to the inappropriate sex hormone may cause permanent changes in their behaviour, we have no way of knowing, for example, how a male rat feels about his role in life when he begins nest-building as presumed result of a single dose of Oestrogen given shortly after birth.

While some studies do indicate some subtle changes in human behaviour following transient exposure to the 'wrong sex' hormones, these must be set against the florid gender-identity states of the human transsexual, which persist in the face of the continuing production of sex hormones in full conformity with the genetic sex.

Curiously, although one would expect to find some Oestrogens produced in the normal male, the oestrogen levels in the MtF TS, prior to hormone therapy, are usually found to be no higher than average.

The prescription drug most commonly used in the treatment of male to female transexed people is Premarin, (conjugated oestrogens extracted from the urine of pregnant mares, hence the name) administered orally, usually 2.5-7.5 mg. daily. The tablets are enteric coated so that they dissolve after passing through the stomach, thus avoiding possible stomach upsets (most oestrogens are gastric irritants).

When compared to contraceptive pills containing oestrogen, this dosage level is extremely high and is usually reduced some time after surgery.

104

Synthetic hormones are much cheaper. The best known is Stilboestrol, which is closely related and has similar biological effects to Oestrogen; but it is liable to cause more side effects than other substances, and is not recommended. Nor is it generally prescribed these days. Other synthetic Oestrogen substitutes are Dienoestrol, Chlorotrianisene and Methylenoestrol. Other Oestrogens usually given in tablet form are Ethinyloestradiol and Mestranol, also used in oral contraceptives.

There are other preparations, including transdermal patches (Estraderm). Other options are Oestrogen implants or depot injections, in solutions which, in the past, have been given as injections, and these are not used in the UK

The Oestrogens normally prescribed are Premarin (usually 2.5mg to 7.5mg daily), or Ethinyloestradiol (50-100mcg. daily).

Progesterone hormones are sometimes prescribed in addition to the regular Oestrogen treatment, either as Provera (5mg to 10mg daily) or Duphaston (Dydrogesterone 10mg to 30mg daily). Androcur (Cyproterone Acetate 50mg to 100mg daily) is also widely used as a testosterone suppressant drug, and an inhibitor of androgen receptors, taken in conjunction with oestrogen. Recently, Levonorgestrel, in conjunction with Ethinyloestradiol (as Ovran) has been prescribed. Levonorgestrel is thought to have a less androgenic effect than other progestogens.

The response of a biological male to oestrogen treatment varies considerably. If, as rarely happens, oestrogens are administered before puberty, a large measure of feminisation can occur. For the post-pubertal pre-operative TS, administered Oestrogens are in continual opposition to naturally produced Androgens such as Testosterone, and they suppress androgen production in the testes.

Post-operative male to female TS's will always need to maintain a low dose of Oestrogens, to provide a reasonable level of female hormones, though of course the dosage will be lower than the pre-operative dosage.

Immediately after resuming hormone treatment post-operatively, it is advised that a reasonably high dosage be maintained for perhaps several months.

The suggested doses are:

FIRST 3 MONTHS POST-OP.

Oestrogens: Premarin 2.5mg twice daily or Ethinyloestradiol 50mcg twice daily or Oestradiol skin patches, such as Estraderm 100, twice weekly.

LONG TERM POST-OP.

Oestrogens: Premarin 2.5mg once daily or Ethinyloestradiol 50 mcg once daily. or Premarin 1.25 once or twice daily. Or Oestradiol skin patches, Estraderm 50 or 100, twice weekly.

Production of the sex steroid hormones is controlled by the pituitary gland. If steroid level in the blood is low the hormone FSH is excreted. This acts as a chemical messenger to stimulate the production of sex steroid hormones. When Oestrogen is administered this partially inhibits FSH production. Often an Anti-androgen (male hormone suppressant) drug is used to cause an artificial lowering of the testosterone levels in a MtF TS, or blocking of testosterone receptors. There is variable reduction in beard growth, or regrowth if electrolysis is undertaken. However the balance of advantage in using Androcur (Cyproterone Acetate) is in doubt.

It can cause unpleasant side effects, including extreme lassitude and depression. As a short term measure a combination of Androcur and Oestrogen may be advantageous. Individual responses to administered Oestrogens with, or without anti-Androgens vary individually from, in rare cases, no noticeable feminising effect, to good results, and likewise from no unwanted side effects to a range of observed problems.

A male to female TS taking customary Oestrogen dosage levels for some years might expect the following physiological effects:

1. Breast development, including enlargement of the nipples and darkening of the areola. After surgery the breasts may continue to increase in size, since the effect of the testes is removed, if suitable dosage is maintained.
2. Increased and redistributed fat deposits cause a rounding of the general figure and hips in particular.
3. A possible increase of weight, and of fluid retention.
4. Improvement of skin tone.
5. Improvement of the condition of scalp hair.

6. The probability of baldness is reduced, but a hairline once receded, will not generally grow back.
7. Beard and body hair may often soften slightly, and the activation of new facial hair follicles may be inhibited.
8. The testes decrease in size.
9. Impotence occurs soon and sterility may follow, after long term Oestrogen administration, which may become permanent in some cases.
10. The penis may atrophy, indeed after exposure to Oestrogens for many years; there may be little material available to surgically create a good depth in the neovagina.

Oestrogen will not:
1. Alter the masculine voice (nor will castration if the voice is deep).
2. Significantly inhibit existing beard growth.
3. Inhibit to a great extent the existing body hair, though it might become finer and appear lighter in colour.

Possible psychological effects include; a decrease in libido, a tendency to weepiness, indecisiveness, and passivity. However it is difficult to disentangle these effects from the emotional response of patients to their overall situation. However, there is evidence that it reduces blood cholesterol.

There are potential dangers to prolonged high doses of Oestrogens, but the drug companies have published almost nothing about this type of patient. The National Formulary and Mims make no references to Transsexuals and Oestrogen administration. These medications in women have been known to have various contraindications, and side effects. There is strong evidence they can contribute to Thromboembolic disease i.e. formation of blood clots. However, in women, Oestrogens are known to protect against cardiovascular accident (stroke) and myocardial infarction (one form of heart attack). There is also a possibility of liver damage, remote with correct dosage. Regular monitoring of blood pressure, and blood tests of liver function, blood lipids and prolactin activity is important.

Please note, retention of the prostate gland after surgery seldom results in prostate trouble in later life, since the gland atrophies without androgens. Similarly the risk of prostate cancer is reduced. However there are rare forms that do not appear to be associated with hormones, and some doctors believe that post operative transwomen should continue periodic examinations. (Which means that they have to reveal themselves, firstly to make their doctor aware they have a prostate, secondly that they now have a neovagina between it and the rectum.)

Few transexed people experience these problems and, although medical follow-up is minimal, it is clear that the benefits of proper psychiatric/hormonal treatment outweigh the risks of no treatment. The risks are relatively low, but real. Exceeding the recommended dose levels significantly increases the risks.

Dr. Asscheman, at the Free University Hospital in Amsterdam, compared four hundred transsexuals on hormones with a control group matched for age. The mortality rate among the transsexuals was four times greater than expected and the causes were not clear. It should be noted that suicide is rare among TS's who are receiving good professional care.

Once breasts develop, there is a slight possibility of breast tumours. If there are pains or lumps in the calves or thighs, or lumps in the breasts this should prompt you to see your GP. Severe chest pains should be treated as an emergency. As we have said, the risks are comparatively low, so there is no need to be unduly anxious, but you should monitor yourself.

Follow up is minimal in most GIC's and GP clinics. There is an optimum level in effective Oestrogen dosage, so taking more will not help you, and may be dangerous.

It is better to take too little rather than too much. Each patient responds differently, and pre- and post-operative needs vary from person to person.

At a more mundane level some patients complain that their nails become brittle and crack easily or form ridges. This endorses work done in the USA, which suggests that high doses of oral Oestrogens inhibit vitamin absorption and metabolism. Calcium supplements and halibut oil and multivitamin may help overcome this problem.

The National Osteoporosis Society has just produced a guidance document: *Transsexualism and Osteoporosis* which is available by post, or may be downloaded from:

http://www.nos.org.uk/documents/TranssexualismandOsteoporosis.doc

52.   Hormones (FtM).

There are hormonal and surgical treatments, which can give a female body a male appearance. The original gene and chromosome composition remains 'female', as does the skeleton. Sadly the person can never actually 'father' a child in the biological sense.

Androgens are the hormones which determine the development of the male physique and of male sexual activity. These steroid hormones are mainly secreted by the testes in a male, and to a lesser extent by the adrenal glands.

In both sexes, the pituitary gland and the hypothalamus control hormone balance. The hypothalamus produces a hormone called LHRH, which influences the production of LH and FSH by the pituitary gland. FSH facilitates the production of sperm in men, and ovulation in women.

The principle human androgen is Testosterone. In women, small amounts are synthesised from Androstenedione. In males, LH stimulates its production in the testes. In a female, LH stimulates ovaries to shed fertile egg cells and it, together with FSH, plays a vital role in maintaining the normal menstrual cycle.

Exogenous (from without) hormones cause the pituitary to reduce production of LH and FSH, responding to the gross level of hormones in the body. Thus, when given to an adult human female, Testosterone can bring about a reduction or cessation of ovarian function, and menstrual bleeding may stop.

Testosterone by tablets (Restandol) or injection (Sustanon) causes irreversible masculinising changes, including hair growth on the body and, later, the face, while head hair may become thinner and the hairs become more brittle. The voice deepens and there may be coarsening of the skin of the face, making it more male-like. Some of these changes may be seen after the menopause, when the ovaries become quiescent, and are due to the small amount of androgens produced by the adrenal gland in a female.

When Testosterone is given to a FtM transexed person, these same changes will occur, with the cessation of ovarian function, but it may take some months before noticeable changes occur. Voice change occurs relatively quickly, often after 2 - 4 months, but it may take some years for the beard to grow fully. There can be no overall growth of bones, in other words, the skeleton does not change with male hormones. Fat distribution may become typically male, and there may be an increase in muscle bulk and power, particularly if the subject exercises intelligently.

Because of the danger of atherosclerosis which may lead to heart attacks, and strokes, and because there is some danger of liver damage if over high doses of androgens (Testosterone) are taken over a long period, one should probably reduce the amount of Testosterone after four or five years.

Bilateral mastectomy, or removal of breasts, is usually required after six to twelve months to facilitate successful cross-gender living. If the breasts are small, this may be done by a small incision around the nipples. If not, a large post-operative scar across the chest used to be inevitable, but surgical techniques have improved greatly.

The ovaries, Fallopian tubes and the uterus should probably be removed, as there is a remote danger of cancer in the long term if they stay in situ. It is considered essential by endocrinologists to continue Testosterone at a maintenance dose post-hysterectomy to prevent loss of Calcium or thinning of the bones (osteoporosis) and other problems, including loss of libido and hot flushes.

It is also advisable to have yearly blood tests for Testosterone level, thyroid and liver function, and blood cell counts and blood lipid tests for atheroma. If hysterectomy is not performed and testosterone is withdrawn, changes such as the deep voice and facial and body hair remain, but periods may sometimes return.

Phalloplasty, the surgical construction of a penis, is best described presently as an experimental procedure. Most patients forgo a procedure, which is still likely to be unsatisfactory, (see later) or protracted and expensive.

53.   Considerations Surrounding Hormones.

In the following section, Jed Bland expresses reservations about what he sees as the myths surrounding hormones for MtF trans people, in the way they are portrayed in the T community, the media and even some technical books.

The prescription of hormones is a controversial area. Some consultants suggest the effects are reversed once medication ceases (for males) Others insist that they are not. Much depends, one supposes, on the dosage and the length of time the person has been taking them. Some say they have a self-diagnostic effect, others deny it. Many cross dressers (and some consultants) are appalled at the idea of a man emasculating himself.

Some consultants will prescribe after the first three months. Others insist on a wait of two years, often after the person has burnt his bridges and transitioned. Some of the latter, however, have been heard to suggest that their patients will have already self-medicated, as if that allows them to cover themselves, and absolves them from responsibility to think about the issues.

There is considerable concern about the many internet pharmacies. While most books on this subject give dire warnings about self-medicating, they rarely go into detail. It is clear that athletes and body-builders take anabolic steroids in spite of the risks, if they can get away with it, and transsexual people are no different. We know that those who are gender dysphoric will still go ahead, but clear information is far better than vague warnings.

There is also a quality problem with hormones from irregular sources. They may be contaminated or simply ineffective. There is also a worrying rise of counterfeit versions of brand name medication. The New England Medical Journal* recently reported that, even with the checks on procurement, samples of a drug which combat anaemia, under the label Procrit were found to be grossly diluted and, in some cases, contained "nothing but Miami tap water.". In February 2004, several Web sites sold unsuspecting consumers contraceptive patches, under the Ortho Evra brand name, that contained no active ingredient.

The main hormones we are concerned with are the so-called gonadal steroids, testosterone and oestradiol. Testosterone is an end product of cholesterol, and is converted as necessary into oestradiol, or into two types of dihydrotestosterone. Type one is best known for its role in male-pattern baldness, while type two seems to be mostly expressed in the prostate where it is involved in male sexuality. However it is increasingly clear that all of the gonadal steroids have other functions all through the body.

The amounts of testosterone produced by males in their testes, and estradiol produced by females in their ovaries, is controlled by a gland at the base of the brain, the pituitary, and a portion of the brain itself, the hypothalamus. As the concentration of gonadal steroids increases so the pituitary reduces production, a so-called 'feedback' mechanism.

There are a number of different classes of drug administered to gender dysphoric people. LHRH analogues act directly on the pituitary, while others such as Androcur block the receptors that testosterone acts upon. The most favoured, because it is not only cheap, but is also the most effective and nearest to naturally occurring body chemicals, is the so-called 'female' hormone, oestradiol in one form or another. It will be clear to the reader that the administration of exogenous (from outside) oestrogen interferes with the feedback mechanism, as it does with the contraceptive pill for women. In males, it causes the pituitary to reduce the output of testosterone from the testes, while the level of oestrogen is increased by the medication.

Bancroft* distinguishes between sexual appetite and sexual interest, the latter being cognitive. The first effect of administering oestrogen, then, is loss of sexual appetite, which some experience as a relief, but it does not affect sexual interest.

The changes in body shape are grossly oversold. There is a website by someone who claims to be a retired medical doctor that has on its homepage a picture reminiscent of the Venus de Milo. There are admittedly helpful changes in the body's metabolism, softening of the skin and hair, with the onset of male pattern baldness being arrested. There is an increase in fat, such as over the pectoral muscles and the lower abdomen, unlike women who tend to put it on their behinds. The emotional effects are more difficult to quantify, and no two people respond in the same way. However, one is never going to look like a page three model from hormones alone. Professor Gooren* of the Free University of Amsterdam suggests that the maximum after two years is a "hemicircumference" of about 18cm, about enough for a 'A' size bra, the exact amount depending on genetic factors, as it does for the person's female siblings. For transsexual people, of course, size isn't everything. It is merely an affirmation of their identity, and those who wish to be more curvaceous have silicone implants.

There are those who think they will be different, and often take excessive doses. Some articles on the subject have quoted a dose rate of oestrogen of up to 40 times more than the naturally occurring level (not forty times the female hrt dose) In fact, when taken orally, most is disposed of by the liver on "first pass." As the dose is increased, there is a saturation point, where the excess is simply excreted, with corresponding damage to the liver.

Which brings us to the less pleasant effects. There is much in the news about the possibility of a slight increase in risk of breast cancer among women taking hormone replacement therapy, which incidentally also applies to the contraceptive pill. Less has been heard about the risk of heart disease, strokes and, particularly, deep vein thromboses, or blood clots in the legs. This may well be less of a problem in someone who is young and fit and takes plenty of exercise. It is also true that most of the effects of hormones have been extrapolated from studies in women. It may also be that, in an androcentric culture, they have been understated in women and overstated in men. However the Free University in Amsterdam has studied transwomen and have confirmed that "the dangers are real."

One reason for medication to be supervised by a general practitioner is said to be that annual blood tests will be provided for liver function and lipid profile. Unfortunately this doesn't usually happen unless the person asks for them, which he is unlikely to do if he feels his medication is at risk.

Another function of medication is to prepare the person physically, as well as psychologically, for the effects of almost total loss of gonadal steroids. It will be apparent from the above that, post-operatively, a transwoman has less testosterone than even someone born female.

It is usual nowadays for the surgeon to fashion a clitoris, although it should be noted that a natural female clitoris is a complex structure, extending deep into the vagina, with about three times as many nerve endings. The nervous system associated with ejaculation is still in place, so many post operative people can experience orgasm, as can those who have had an orchidectomy, if they wish to. However it is clear that this must be cognitively rather than hormonally driven.

It is quite clear that there are those who have always been at odds with their body and the gender label that has been imposed on them. It is equally clear that there are those who, for whatever reason, are in conflict with the gender role in which they are living. The reduction in sexual appetite brought about by medication may well give a respite in which people can more clearly assess their motivations. The bottom line is that the diagnosis depends on a life history account which the psychiatrist has no way of confirming. Each person's transition therefore is entirely their own responsibility.

Rudolf, P.M., Bernstein, I. B.G. (2004) *Counterfeit Drugs,* New England Journal of Medicine, 2004 Number 14, 350:1384-1386

Bancroft J. (1989) *Human Sexuality and its Problems,* Edinburgh: Churchill Livingstone

Henk Assheman MD and Louis J. G. Gooren MD. (1996) *Hormone Treatment in Transexuals.* GENDYS '96, The Fourth International Gender Dysphoria Conference, Manchester England. *Ed* Purnell. A., London: Gendys Conferences.

54.   The Non-Surgical Solution … Living Transgendered.

There is, for some, a non-surgical solution. If elderly, very obese, suffering from various conditions like diabetes, heart problems, circulatory problems, there may be a medical rationale for not opting for full surgery. These transgenderists have a right to be taken seriously. Because of the poor 'state of the art', and the long series of operations necessary for the FtM to gain a 'good penis' many trans-men stop surgery at the post hysterectomy and mammectomy stage. Phalloplasty is not easily performed, few surgeons in the UK are skilled or experienced in their area of reconstructive surgery.

Using skin grafts several surgeons are providing a reasonable phallus for these men, but the surgical process is often in several stages and is expensive,

Clitoral orgasm is quite satisfactory for many FtM's. Under the influence of androgens the clitoris responds by enlarging, sometimes to 1.5 inches long or so. By manipulation this can provide very satisfactory orgasms for the new-man. He has to stimulate his partner by other means than full penetration.

In the case of the MtF, the largely gender motivated aetiology means that amputation of the penis and testes without the creation of neo-vagina can be 'enough'.

This is sometimes known as the 'cosmetic operation' - in that it means, apart from sexual activity, the pubic area looks quite reasonable, and the "offending organ" is no longer there.

Many 'ordinary' women and men have to learn to compromise in their own circumstances.

Happiness is not a deep vagina or a large penis - it is being a whole person who loves, and is loved, and who loves her/himself in a reasonable balanced way. We surely are in no position to form a hierarchy of those who are have's and have-not's, or those who have good surgery or poor, or those who are satisfied with what they have and those who are never satisfied.

However as a client population the TS does have rights, and among them is the right to have the best possible surgery, or not as the case may be, to best suit her or his own circumstances.

Some MtF patients request castration (bilateral orchidectomy) as a first stage, or as a sufficient move towards an enhanced body image.

55.   Gender Reassignment Surgery (GRS).
= SEX REASSIGNMENT SURGERY (SRS)
= GENDER AFFIRMATION SURGERY

Surgery (MtF) - Vaginoplasty.
Choice of surgeon is an important factor. There are too few surgeons who are appropriately skilled and trained in these procedures. Those who do get referred for this surgery find that in the NHS the waiting lists are long. A wait of three years or more is not unusual, even if the criteria for surgery are all fulfilled. There are often logjam waiting lists. Sometimes it is impractical to opt for surgery to create a pseudo-vagina, and Vaginoplasty is not always performed.

a) The "Cosmetic" Operation. If circumstances dictate this may be performed; a radical Orchidectomy and Penectomy (castration and removal of the penis), with retained scrotal tissue used to form labia. Since the penis is removed, the urethra exits in a more or less suitable position. This surgery may or may not involve penetration of the perineum providing an anchor to draw the labia down to give an appearance of a vaginal entrance. This operation is perhaps best performed by a plastic surgeon, with Urology experience.

b) Vaginoplasty. (Surgical creation of a pseudo-vagina.) The patient seeking a functional vagina should realise several things.

A surgeon has to work with what material is available. Anatomies vary, and, most important, the surgeon's first duty is to preserve life, to maintain the good health and prognosis of, and for, the patient. Finally, if possible, to provide the patient with the best practical solutions in terms of function and sensation and appearance.

To hope for a sensational (in both senses!), functional vagina, which lubricates, looks right, and is indistinguishable from the 'real thing' is asking rather a lot. Some 'post-op's' and surgeons do seem to have achieved this. In the UK, a single stage Vaginoplasty is usually performed. In this scrotal and some penile skin is utilised to form the neovagina, having performed orchidectomy and removed all but the penile stump. The prostate remains in situ. The meatus (the exit hole of the urine via the urethra) usually was perforate to that penile stump, in most surgery performed until the mid-eighties, and the urethra is not re-sited, by surgeons using older methods of surgery.

The best surgery does now, in the UK, result in the penile stump being reduced and the urethra re-sited. When possible, a **Clitoroplasty** is performed using a small piece of the corpus spongeosum, nerve and blood supply from the penis to form this.

A relatively realistic vagina is formed of inverted penile and scrotal skin pushed into a canal created anterior to the rectum. Enlightened surgeons will remove most of the penile stump, and re-site the meatus, which is why a skilled urologist is perhaps most adept at this method.

Because penile and scrotal tissue is used in this method it is important that not too much time on high Oestrogen levels pre-op be maintained since atrophy of this material takes place. Also obviously the 'Cosmetic Operation' should not be performed if plastic reconstruction of a neovagina were envisaged. Should this have happened, or if there be major problems with "size", other material (colonic or skin grafts) will be required.

In the past, a split-skin graft was taken from the thigh and the vagina so constructed was inserted through the perineal wall and placed against the rectal cavity. A vaginal form was needed, permanently held in place by a T-bandage, to prevent the vagina from atrophying.

This, so-called type 'A' vaginoplasty operation, employing a split-skin graft, passed through the perineum, as a second stage, places the neovagina is in an incorrect, even dangerous position. This outdated method, still used by some plastic surgeons, should be avoided.

If remedial work is required a **Drop-pedicle Colon Graft** may help. A section of colon (large intestine), with its blood supply is detached from the large intestine and connected to the pseudo-vagina, creating a 'functional', deep, muscular vagina. The advantage of this is more material is available for greater depth and there is no hair on the inside of this tube. There are drawbacks, not least a scar.

If the penis is very small, or circumcision has taken place, this is probably the procedure of choice for vaginal construction. Few UK surgeons perform modern single stage Gender Confirmation surgery. This type of surgery could involve the skills of an urologist, a plastician, a microsurgeon or a bowel surgeon; or preferably a surgeon with all these skills.

So-called 'sex-change' surgery is contentious, and has some level of risk. Surgery is, or should only be, performed after proper assessment and referral by an experienced psychiatrist.

Surgical results can vary; the male body was not developed to accommodate a vagina. TS's can be unrealistic and difficult patients who think a vagina needs to be a foot deep! However, an unhelpful and chauvinistic view by a surgeon that "any old hole will do" does not serve the needs or rights of his patient. Above all in requesting this type of surgery, a patient is in the role of potentially being made 'whole', or being made much worse. The surgeon is in a very powerful position to provide his skill and expertise to enhance quality of life. There are potential liabilities, but the patient has rights. The surgeon also needs protection, not least by consent form, and by indemnities. This is why the patient is usually expected to be over eighteen and single. Some surgeons install an upper age limit for this surgery because of increased risk of complications.

Pre-operative precautions.

These usually include discontinuing the hormone therapy for some weeks before surgery, and during recovery, although not all surgeons adopt this practice. Antibiotics are often prescribed during healing. The 'pre-op' preparation often involves a clear liquid-only diet (essential if

117

colonic implant is to be utilised for construction of the neovagina), and always the patient is 'nil by mouth' overnight the day before surgery.

Pain can be avoided if an epidural be installed, otherwise painkillers are reasonably effective during recovery.

Post-operative care.

Hospitalisation is normally approximately 6 to 14 days, usually 10 days, complications excepted. Return to work is normally in six to eight weeks. It is best to be a non-smoker, so give up before surgery if possible is good advice, after surgery it is still wise. It also helps if you are not obese.

During surgery the neovagina will have been packed with gauze. This, and the urinary catheter (which will have been inserted before surgery starts), and the stitches will be removed, over the next few days. Careful hygiene is important and twice-daily warm saline bathes are often advised. The nursing staff or surgeon will advise with a care plan.

Help should normally be given to show the patient how to lubricate, dilate (stretch) the neovagina. The vaginal aperture needs this process of dilation to prevent it stenosing (closing up). The usual dilation regime would be twice daily for about 20 minutes. There may be some discomfort initially, but this should ease off in time.

It is not unusual for there to be some time needed before a 'tidy stream' of urine can be passed, and sometimes the meatus (the opening of the urethra) may need some stretching by the surgeon (as it heals it sometimes tends to close up a little.) The labia should be kept clean and dry, it is wise to avoid scented soaps at this time. Sanitary towels will help soak up any pus or blood loss especially after dilation.

Dr. White's C2 maternity towels seem popular for this period of recovery, but a switch to a lighter product later seems usual. The genital area will be swollen and tender post-op', but should settle down after six weeks or so.

There are problems which could be serious if not dealt with:

1. Severe difficulty in, or pain when, passing urine; complete inability to micturate (pass urine) must be treated as an emergency. (Recatheterisation, or stretching the meatus with stents will resolve this painful and dangerous possible complication).

2. Infections are, unfortunately, not rare. Discharges, extreme swelling, pain; discoloration may (in some cases with pyrexia - a high temperature) show there is an infection. Antibiotics should resolve this problem.

It should be safe to have intercourse (safe sex) two to three months post-op' assuming dilation and complications do not indicate otherwise. The surgeon should advise. Hygienic and sensible use of a sterilised plastic dilator (under direction of the surgeon/nursing staff ... (or use of a gradually inflated sac technique) might be employed to keep the neovagina patent (open).

Private costs for surgery vary, but in the UK, £4,500-£7,000 seems to be the range of price of surgery at this time, including, or excluding, clinic fees. It would seem surgery performed by some surgeons in the UK is some way behind that available in the States, Netherlands and Switzerland. Surgeons in Thailand are getting good cosmetic results.

It is wise for a patient to ask the surgeon which method he uses, which results he expects, and for a realistic assessment of what is both possible and suitable. It is foolish to be obsessed with depth of the vagina. Normal female anatomy gives a depth of about five inches (12 cms).

Too often in the past an 'MtF TS' found herself with floppy labia, or a large penile stump which gave pain during intercourse and looked wrong. The patient's (and her surgeon's) aim should surely be to achieve for her a 'female' appearance and function as far as possible. However, she should also realise that there are limits as to what can actually be done.

There are surgeons, and 'new-women', who say that a properly surgically constructed vagina can appear 'genuine' to a partner, and that vaginal orgasm is possible. The surgeon has, as part of his duty to his patient, to try to provide her with a convincing and functional vagina. Unfortunately it is not possible with some anatomies, and certain surgeons are more successful than others in helping their patient become as far as she might, a 'whole woman'

A patient can request a minimal penile stump (it erects painfully, if too large). Some surgeons fashion a 'clitoris' (Clitoroplasty) from a residual portion of corpus spongeosum; some perform a 'Z' or a 'W' plasty, to provide a neat 'V' shaped labial juncture above the vagina.

Post-operatively, vaginal sensation seems to vary. There can be problems if the vaginal cavity has hair growing in it.

Whatever, if function, sensation, and appearance are all good, and orgasm is achievable, the new-woman may still have many difficulties to face. To enjoy what is, and what can be, done is more constructive than to be obsessed with any imperfections.

Some Medical/Surgical Terms Used here:

Agonadal	Without testes or ovaries
Bilateral Orchidectomy	Removal of both testes
BP	Blood Pressure
DVT	Deep Vein Thrombosis
Dilation	Stretching
Genitoplasty	Reconstruction of the genitals
Haematomas	Large blood blisters
Hirsute	Hairy
Meatus	Opening through which we pass water
Micturate	Pass water
Morbidity	Ill effects
Neo-clitoris	Transplant of an area at the tip of the penis to create a hopefully sensitive clitoris
Osteoporosis.	loss of Calcium resulting in brittle bones
Prolapse	a falling down or slipping out of place
Prosthetic testes	Artificial testes
Pylonephritis.	An inflammation of the kidney/s often caused by infection
Stent	a conical stretching device
Urethra	The tube which carries the urine from the bladder to pass water

56. Surgery MtF - Outcome and Prognosis.

Surgical Problems Following MtF Gender Reassignment Surgery.

Talk presented by Mr Philip Thomas, Consultant Surgeon, Brighton Nuffield Hospital. Report of his Paper at Gendys Conference 2002, by Alice Purnell RGN, BSc, PGDC

Patients often fail to listen to what could go wrong, because they are excited by the prospect of at last getting the operation they want. It is vital that patients understand the issues prior to signing a Consent to what is elective surgery, and that she is prepared for any adverse reactions, thereby reality reduces anxiety. She has an important role in post op' care, so should follow the surgeon's advice.

All surgery is subject to possible complications. Fortunately there have been no fatalities in the UK and at most no more than 20% have any problems and these are generally easily rectified.

During the surgery, bleeding is rarely a problem, none have needed transfusions.

The blood supply to the scrotal skin flaps and the neo-clitoris is vulnerable since very small blood vessels are involved.

The proximity of the rectum to the inverted skin tube needs to be carefully avoided and is easily rectified if nicked. This has not occurred in Brighton, but in such a case a colostomy might be required in worst case scenario.

Urethral bleeding could occur from the stump, but this is easily cauterised.

Occasionally labial bruising or haematoma may occur.

Any infections should be managed by the GP, providing antibiotics.

Recurrent cystitis or pylonephritis has occurred in some cases and should be dealt with on a case by case basis.

Inability to micturate can be addressed by re-catheterisation or the use of stents.

After 3 months generally things have settled down, swelling should have reduced and healing completed.

In perhaps 5% of cases there may be problems arising from scarring or narrowing of the urethral opening, which can be alleviated, as a day case, by dilation of the meatus.

In the early stages proper use of the vaginal dilator is vital, and proper training in this procedure is very important, those who do not dilate end up with a narrow vagina.

Sometimes there is scarring and some narrowing of the vagina post op'.

Several patients' experience bulging of the back wall of the vagina (3%), and a few may prolapse. This can be repaired, by stitching and pulling up the vagina; depth is not lost this way.

121

If too much tissue is retained in the neo-clitoris erectile tissue around the urethra may cause a prominence which can be troublesome, so it is important to take away enough tissue, whilst hopefully allowing this to retain sensitivity, further surgery may offer a solution to this.

Hair in the vagina and discharges tend to go together, so perhaps clearing the scrotal skin of hair will be useful in hirsute cases.

It is hard to predict sensation, realistically a patient may have to face a life without orgasm, but this is unusual and so far nobody has opted not to go ahead on this basis alone.

A realistic concept of depth is important, 4 inches is normal and adequate.

Good nursing care is very important; nurses need to be able to teach the patient dilation and aftercare. Good advice optimises a good outcome. Removal of the pack is important and generally should be supervised by the surgeon or a fully experienced nurse. Confidence is important and over enthusiastic dilation is not a good idea.

Smoking and obesity do reduce the safety of surgery (DVT, haematomas and prolapse); also fat around the area of surgery makes it hard to get good depth.

HIV and sickle cell anaemia will increase the likelihood of infections and complications and will need special care.

At Charing Cross they do not operate on the obese or smokers. Risk of a poor outcome is increased with age and in the case of diabetics.

A single stage operation is the norm in the UK, however follow-up revisional surgery does generally resolve most problems.

Careful consideration is needed with the colo-vaginoplasty, since it is more radical than the scrotal skin flap vaginoplasty.

Four out of five have no surgical problems, but it is important that a full informed consent be understood and given.

57.   Orchidectomy.

"Is there a Role for Bilateral Orchidectomy as a Preliminary Procedure Prior to Full Genitoplasty in MtF Patients?"

From Talk given by Mr. Tim Terry, Consultant Surgeon, Urology, University Hospital Leicester. No paper submitted, report by Alice Purnell RGN, BSc, PGDC

Mr Terry has worked at Leicester since 1992 and in the first 3 years performed about 100 bilateral orchidectomy surgical procedures on GD people, more are now going for full surgery, knowing probably that with increased experience a surgeon's reputation increases.

There seem to be benefits in psychological and hormonal changes after this operation, as well as anatomical, there being a slight reduction of the scrotal bulge.

There is no change to the voice, but male pattern baldness may reduce, and in time body hair may reduce. Distribution of muscle and body fat will be similar to that of a eunuch.

This surgery is irreversible, after it a patient will of course be infertile and since the testes produce 95% of testosterone so the patient will probably entirely lose erections.

In the agonadal there is a result similar to Androgen Deficiency Syndrome with several effects a patient should be aware of prior to surgery.

Muscle bulk will reduce over the years, anaemia can be a problem, reduced uptake of Calcium can occur resulting in reduced bone density (increased risk of Osteoporosis) together with changes in fat distribution and skin quality.

There are pluses and minuses to consider.

There is also the cost to the NHS or the patient of an extra surgical procedure.

The cost of an extra procedure should be weighed against that of replacing the use of antiandrogens to reduce testosterone and there may be some morbidity (haematoma or pain).

However this is sometimes useful to a patient who can not wait for the full surgery, wishes to reduce male pattern baldness, or the regrowth of facial hair if undergoing electrolysis or who is elderly and does not perhaps have concerns about sexual activity.

Young patients may need to consider storing sperm prior to this surgery.

Feminising hormones reduce the amount of scrotal tissue available for genitoplasty. It is a myth that orchidectomy alone will do this.

Bilateral Orchidectomy is performed as a day case, using a vertical scrotal incision. There should be at least a 6-month wait prior to GRS if this is the plan.

There are costs and risks and side effects reported for all medications, these need to be considered prior to informed consent from the patient commencing them, as well as prior to any surgery - a realistic informed decision needs to be obtained from all patients.

To reduce Testosterone, synthetic anti-androgens (Cyproterone Acetate = Androcur) is usually used, or a 5α reductase inhibitor (Finasteride) in some cases. Androcur can in some cases affect liver function, or cause depression, or other effects. Flutamide, a hormone antagonist, causes acute diarrhoea in some 20% of patients.

LHRH Analogues over stimulate the pituitary switching off production of testosterone. These can be given as 3 monthly injections (which cost £350).

Orchidectomy costs about £600.

Those opting for Orchidectomy, having been assessed and fully informed are treated as day cases, under local anaesthetic, with no need for starving prior to surgery, no need for general anaesthetic in almost all cases.

They may be anxious, so might need Diazepam. It is a good idea if a friend collects them after the surgery. They go home after 2 hours.

There will be an i/v line during surgery.

The patient will be discharged with absorbable sutures, a small dressing and pain control.

It is a very straightforward procedure. There is a very low morbidity (= bad side effects).

There is a case for this as a staging procedure, replacing use of drugs to reduce testosterone levels and as a means of an alternative to waiting a very long time for GRS.

It is sometimes hard for a clinician to put himself entirely in the shoes of a patient, so it is important to listen and to be flexible. Physical and psychological aspects must not be underestimated.

Fully informed patients choose what they want pragmatically taking personal responsibility for this. A good result is a patient who understands that things can go wrong, but you have to deal with it. Realism is vital.

Mr Terry was asked to perform this procedure on a man who had to continue to appear male at work who requested orchidectomy but with insertion of prosthetic testes as a means of stopping testosterone.

We need much more research and training both for endocrinologists and the prescribing psychiatrists.

58.   Surgery (FtM).

Mammectomy, Mastectomy, Hysterectomy, Phalloplasty, Scrotoplasty

A number of surgical procedures are required. The removal of breasts, and removal of the internal generative organs of a woman are standard surgical procedures.

However, phalloplasty (surgical construction of a penis) is much more specialised and experimental and results vary greatly.

1. Mastectomy. Bilateral simple mastectomy is performed. The nipples should be preserved. These are usually larger than those of a typical man are, so (if applicable) areolar reduction should be requested. It is almost inevitable that there will be some degree of scarring after this surgery; but, if a circular areolar incision were performed, scarring should be minimal. This should itself be hidden by chest hair with good luck. A simple mastectomy should not leave radical scarring and the patient is advised to discuss nipple preservation with his surgeon.

2. Hysterectomy. The ovaries, uterus, cervix, and Fallopian tubes will usually be removed. A gynaecological surgeon will have performed this operation on numerous women for a number of reasons, so there should be no special technical problems. The bladder and urethral opening would not be touched, and they would function post-operatively just as before. If the patient is considering having a phalloplasty it is better to have a vertical hysterectomy scar than an horizontal one, so potential skin graft donor sites are not compromised.

3. Phalloplasty. (Surgical construction of a penis) Surgeons are experimenting and developing techniques, there is no standard method.

Since 1985, methods are being developed in the USA, where one stage microvascular surgery is being employed. In general, Phalloplasty involves several stages of surgery, and many problems exist. A penis is constructed from material (skin, muscle, nerves, blood supply etc.) taken from another site on the body (usually the abdomen, groin, thigh or forearm).

These grafts are by means of a complex series of manoeuvres originally developed by plastic surgeons for replacing lost or damaged tissues after trauma, or burns, the aim being to keep the blood supply patent, the graft to 'take' and (if possible) for sensation, appearance and function to be good. Infection should also be prevented.

If skin on the donor site is hairy, it is advisable to have the hair permanently removed prior to surgery. This 'replanted' skin flap is often used to form a double layered tube of skin with skin lining the urethral extension within the penis. This has to attach in such a way as to be completely leak proof, and must not shrink with scarring. There may be some problems resulting from the recurrent passage of urine through this tube lined with what is essentially skin (unless a tube of bladder tissue is used to line the extended urethra).

Without a prosthesis (a temporary, or a permanent stiffening implant, usually made of silastic or silica), or as in the past using a section of rib or cartilage, which remains permanently 'erect', there is no suitable equivalent to the erection process, which is due to blood flow into the corpus spongeosum, and corpus cavernosum. The situation is improving, and the technology, which has helped impotent and injured men, has now provided a number of prosthetic solutions, including an indwelling inflatable prosthesis.

The technically most difficult aspect of surgery seems to be concerning the construction of the urethra, which may be formed of various material from the patient's own body (e.g.. a section of ileum, of gracilis muscle from the thigh, vaginal muscle, or possibly best, of bladder tissue). Sometimes instead synthetic materials are used. With these types of surgery there is some risk of urinary infection, strictures or fistulas (blockages or leaks) during these numerous constructive processes.

4. *Scrotoplasty* may be performed at the same time as phalloplasty. The labia majora are sewn together to form scrotal sacs, and silicone prosthetic testicular implants are inserted.

Before surgery, or administration of male hormones, the person would be referred after proper assessment, by a psychiatrist skilled in the field of gender identity. Sadly few NHS surgeons are prepared to devote time and resources to this complex problem. There are a few unscrupulous private surgeons who may take money and use the FtM TS as an unknowing guinea pig. It is important to understand clearly what is being attempted, and what may eventually be gained.

Perfection is the rainbow's end, a goal that can never be reached; an acceptable compromise must be sought.

Reference: "The White Book" by S.T. Whittle PhD via FTM Network London WC1N3XX

59. Some Cosmetic Options - Mammoplasty. Breast enlargement Rhinoplasty (Nose reshaping).

As well as 'the op' there are various cosmetic operations which might be provided on the NHS if the psychiatrist assesses a real need. For private cosmetic work it is not necessary to be referred by a psychiatrist, but care should be taken in choice of surgeon.

The MtF TS most frequently opts for surgery to enlarge the breasts if in her view they are not 'right'; to adapt the shape of the nose; or in some cases to try to improve on a large Adam's apple.

1. Mammoplasty. Breast enlargement, involves implanting a breast enlarging prosthesis, or substance to enlarge a flat chest. It costs between five and eight hundred pounds (1990).

In the past Silicone injections were used, before the prosthesis was developed, but the 'breasts' often relocated into inappropriate sites and there has been considerable litigation in the States because of the distress and medical problems this could cause.

The implant is a seamless bag, having a rough surface on the side to site against the chest wall, and filled with a fluid gel (bio-inactive surgical Silicone) or saline. This is inserted via small curved incisions, about two inches long, along the line of the breast fold so visible scarring should be minimal. Hospitalisation should be for up to 48 hours.

Keloids (angry red scars) have been reported in a very few cases. These enlarged 'boobs' do actually look man-made if they are too big.

They 'stand up' when their owner lies down. A balanced ideal should be sought. It should be realised that you save money if you have implants at the time of genital surgery, but breasts often grow after the removal of the gonads, so there could be a danger of being top heavy.

2. Rhinoplasty (Nose reshaping). An experienced plastic surgeon can often radically improve on nature by reshaping the nose. This costs from around £1000 (including clinic fees) There should be no scarring. Hospitalisation (clinic stay) is rarely more than 24 hours, and is sometimes not required. A plaster cast is left in situ over the nose for about a week, and the patient looks like 'Dracula's daughter' for about a fortnight. Hopefully she looks better when the swelling and bruising abate. It is advisable not to wear heavy glass-lensed spectacles until 'The New Nose' has settled down. The new shape will be apparent in about two months.

3. Reduction of the Adam's Apple. Is often requested but rarely performed. The thyroid cartilage supports the larynx and, being cartilage, is slow to heal, responding unpredictably to surgery.

This is sometimes performed together with trimming the vocal cords. However results seem to vary in terms of vocal quality after this.

The quest for 'perfection' leads a few rare affluent trans women to become 'plastic surgery junkies'. For those with the means, and a few with the necessity, other procedures are available including jaw remodelling, dermabrasion (removing electrolysis scars usually), skin peeling, hair transplants, and so on. It has been said that if a patient still has her own teeth she might be better advised to spend her money with a good dentist … that is, assuming they like each other.

To be serious, of course some things need surgical interventions. Most women, (and men) might perhaps spend a great deal to look like the IDEAL woman (or man), but perhaps some energy should go towards not being too self concerned or absorbed, again a balance.

N.B. Never have Silicon injected it is dangerous!

60. Social Changeover.

There are a number of choices, which affect how one can cope with these changes, and what these changes are to be. Where you live? Do you stay put or move? If the choice is to stay in the same accommodation there will be those around who know or guess at the situation. From some will be sympathy, curiosity, and encouragement; from others hostility, ridicule or indifference.

Loneliness and an increasing sense of isolation may occur, particularly if the family is very hostile. This worry may beset the TS new to her or his role. There is a high price to pay. A change of home, or of work, or unemployment, means more stress and new challenges. If the decision is to stay in the same employment, colleagues will know of the changeover, and might harass the TS or cause difficulties for her or his employer.

Armed with appropriate documentation, name, clothes, hairstyle, the 'Life Test' expected by the GIC's does not in any way prepare the 'new-man or woman' for their new life. Neither can it provide an 'appropriate' past life.

Who to tell? Who not to trust? How to 'create an appropriate childhood'? There are many problems but, with luck, psychotherapy, counselling, support groups and (above all) good friends, much can be done to help. While changeover is in progress it is sometimes a good idea to start a new training, a course of study, or further education in the 'new life mode.' The momentum of doing this should help distract from self-absorption and isolation. Support groups can help in this way both before and after surgery.

If the family has split up this might be irrevocable, but many estranged ex-spouses, and, more particularly, children, do reach understanding, given time.

At least two years are often needed to heal the wounds. The Gender Dysphoric person is often blamed for the disruptions to her, or his, family. If not blamed by them, she often blames herself. Few of those who are hostile or hypercritical examine why they adopt such an unreasoned view. Some TS's over-dramatise their plight, or their own courage. Others will make their own judgements, valid or otherwise. It is not a matter of scoring points but of getting on with life.

Learning to deal with members of one's 'original sex' can be frightening, tedious or funny. The ploys some men use to 'lure' a girl to bed are such dreadful clichés, which as a teenager, a TS might be ashamed to admit she used, and certainly heard other men use. Listening to a man lay down the law about a subject she knows far more about herself is something many women have encountered, and they have to learn to abide it, or to raise objections, or be assertive.

To somehow switch sides in the battle of the sexes can feel like being on the right side, but it can also bring an understanding of both sides.

Problems do not cease after surgery. Needs include love, companionship, work, goals, family, a sense of humour, and self-esteem. Too many TS's see the 'Operation' as the answer to all their problems - it looms so large. It is a part of the answer to some of their problems, if they are genuinely transexed. But for those who have made a mistake in self-diagnosis it becomes a problem. This is why the long haul of waiting, learning, adjusting, and testing the 'life role experience', although beset with difficulties and 'Catch 22' situations, is very necessary.

Thoughtlessness of others, breaking confidences, especially by other trans people, who see it as a matter of supreme pride to announce their changeover, and those of all they know, can be painful. Generally these individuals do not 'pass' successfully in public in their desired role, but this does make many gender dysphoric persons disenchanted with the lunatic fringe of the 'Trannie' world, often resulting in turning one's back on one's 'brothers and sisters' from the TS subculture.

Most people get on with their lives; but the depression - whether it is endogenous, or exogenous (from inside or outside) - that most trans people feel, results in, or some might say arises from, a total form of self-absorption. This is counterproductive. There are others with problems in the world - those with other disabilities, difficult lives, isolation and worries.

A defiant attitude may get people to notice, and 'Society' to change slowly, or quickly in a negative, or a positive way to the Transperson.

A strident or uncaring attitude from the TS can damage the TS cause and case. A lack of concern for others is not helpful. All people have a right to move through life with pride, but also to bring sincerity and generosity to those around us; to learn to smile and to laugh. The human condition is, after all, an extraordinary adventure

61.   Diversity and Respect.

Once a person has resolved to accept their life in terms of gender by being whichever type of transperson they may or may not be, it is important to leave the ghetto of being 'TRANS'. Get on with life. Respect others and claim it for yourself.

Trans is only one aspect of Diversity.

Diversity is a normal aspect of nature and difference must be respected but need not divide us …

As individuals our thoughts can inspire or crush us, as can the words and actions of others. Life is not a dream, nor should it be a nightmare or a prison …

Mutual respect and acceptance of diversity is important. We need to stand up for each other as well as ourselves and take care not to introduce forms of oppression amongst ourselves. It is always important to offer respect to others, and the various types of T people.

There should be no pecking order, the 'ordinary man or woman' is not 'better than' the intersexed person, nor are they themselves 'better than' the TS, TG or TV, just different…

The first step to take is pride in oneself. Far too many T people feel shame or guilt about their position and collude with the oppressors by failing to expect the respect they deserve.

Traditionally there have been problems between intersexed and T people, between TV's and TS's and the resulting in-fighting simply abets the rule of oppressors.

To not be a victim or a part of this oppression one does need to feel secure enough as oneself, so as to not see others who are different as threats, or react unkindly to them and their 'difference'.

This problem has been promoted by the lack of public and personal information so that all 'different' people were tarred with the same brush. For example all T people of whatever 'type' have been seen as deviant, gay, sex maniacs, harmful to children, crazy and so on. Most are actually fairly conventional apart from their gender thing. Marginalization of gay people is not now acceptable. Diversity is celebrated.

Surely it is best to be proud of oneself and to be anti-oppression rather than anti a particular group or person. We do need to speak and stand against tyrants and bigots. Let us not ourselves be bigots.

I would hope that those who see themselves as Trans-anything feel secure enough in themselves so as not to believe they are superior or inferior to others.

Diversity is the in spin-word.

It is true that a cross-dresser has little in common with a transexed person, save that each is oppressed.

The Women's Movement and Gay, GLBT, and Disabled Pride have all helped the cause of those seeking recognition and equality for minorities and to challenge inequalities. Pride marches take place in London, Manchester and Brighton for example. They all now celebrate GLBT. They are not simply for gay men.

A sense of sisterhood and brotherhood will get things done and hopefully eliminate public fear that THEY will frighten the horses, or upset our patriarchal society and the foundations of family life!

It is important that minorities are mutually supportive. If one is intolerant of others how can one expect respect?

What can not be tolerated is muddled thinking - those who think to be a gay person, or Transexed, or a Cross-dresser, or a Transgenderist, or a Pervert are all the same is simply ignorant.

To be English, Scottish, Irish or French is to be different in certain ways. They are all European Countries with different history, sometimes different languages, and a pride in those differences.

Each of the Trans groups come from a 'separate country' and history. Some have mutual borders. Together they can achieve more than alone.

62. Trans people, Language and the Legal Mess.

Society and medicine do, to a limited extent accept the need for reassignment surgery in some cases, and yet the SOC persists in leaving the postoperative woman or man with the label "transsexual", instead of as a woman or man. This merely reinforces the legal limbo trans people were left with. If you had a hair lip repair in childhood, you are not "a hair lip" as an adult person. You had a hair lip. It is part of your past, which can affect your future and present, you have a scar, but it does not describe who or what you now are.

The "classic transsexual" person who had surgery is still in a legal straightjacket and denied normal human rights in many countries. Once these men and women have resolved their gender dysphoria they should surely not be defined as "transsexuals" by anyone unless they so wish. They are simply women or men who have overcome this difficulty.

What of the law? To call it an ass is to do a disservice to quadrupeds. The beneficiaries of the mess it is in are usually the lawyers, but it can and will serve us. It is clear that a large group of European people is denied human rights because of the Birth Certificate issues. These are not only in respect of marriage.

I participated in Amsterdam at the 23rd. Colloquy on European Law, on "Transsexualism, Medicine and Law" in April 1993. There it was estimated that worldwide at a conservative estimate, there must be at least 60,000,000 gender dysphoric people. We have crazy situations in the U.K. and the Republic of Ireland where it is legal for a new woman to marry a woman (yet lesbian marriages are not recognised) if her birth certificate stills says "boy". However such a marriage might be void since consummation is seen as penetration (phallocrats!).

Incidentally nobody is "born a man", or "born a woman" - they are born as a baby.

Pressure is growing to harmonise the legal status of 'new women and men' (I shall not call them transsexuals). The U.K. is obliged to recognise marriages in other E.U. Member States. We do so of their citizens, but did not do this for our citizens until the Gender Recognition Act 2004.

It depends where one was born as to what is their legal sex/gender in that case. In the Netherlands a person with amended birth certificate can step across the unmanned border into Belgium and still be regarded as legally a man. A small step for a man and a great step for womankind? Developments in European Law had a potential, which would not only affect the status of new-men and new-women, but of women and men in general in terms of inheritance, pensions, and partnerships.

Hopefully soon all European Countries will eventually stop resisting these changes and will comply with common sense solutions.

I believe that once the legal mess sorts itself out medicine will be propelled towards a more empathetic view of the transexed person.

Why can not *any* couple who love each other and want to share a life together be permitted to marry? Now the State marries people, why can it not permit equal rights to all couples? This would mean a couple who were originally married could remain so after the trans person has completed changeover with a Birth Certificate which recognises her/his gender.

But let us face facts, Governments simply express poorly hidden discrimination by their homophobic legal barriers.

63. The Legal Block to Full Acceptance - Prior to the Gender Recognition Act (2004).

Has meant that transition and treatment were incomplete until 2004/5.

Christine Goodwin won her battle in the European Court of Human Rights, to which the UK are signatories, to be recognised as a woman and to marry under British law.

The judgement in Strasbourg was unanimous, that *"The UK's failure to recognise her new identity in law breached her rights to respect for private life and her right to marry, under the European Convention on Human Rights."* With all that is happening in politics the move towards equality for T people still seemed to be dreadfully slow. There did not seem to be a sense of urgency, since I suppose governments are nervous of backlash from something that will win them few votes. The rights of the fox were, it seems, more appealing than a few sad outsiders to the phobic masses with their fear of gender anarchy. Oddly the Bill passed without a whimper.

Since the April Ashley Ruling (1970) there have been great legal and practical discrepancies in respect of T people, which will no longer be tolerated. By demanding equal rights with the rest of society, some Trans people have gained full legal acceptance, meaning that our Laws, in England and Wales, and in Scotland and in N. Ireland, the Isle of Man and the Channel Isles will now have to accord with this ruling in fact and in spirit. This is a victory for common sense over bigotry and fear.

We should remember all those who have suffered injustice, depression, fear, discrimination, committed suicide, or been marginalized. The dripping tap of discrimination can become equivalent to the Chinese Water Torture.

We should remember many of those of the T community who, over the last 40 years, were not strong enough and took their own lives.

Times are changing, thank God. But there is still much to do to bring UK Law into the 21st Century. As things stood before the Bill:

- Marriage was unlawful.
- Originally recorded gender remained on all NI records and Death Certificates.
- Detainment and imprisonment rights were not assured.
- Rape of female TS people was not chargeable as such.

(some still do in the Isle of Man and the Channel Isles. All do still stand in the Republic of Ireland)

The Law was against accepting facts and had created a group of people who were denied normal human rights before the Gender Recognition Act as a result of the April Ashley Case 1970. Before April's Case, Birth Certificates could be and were amended for a post-operative individual with a transexed past. This has meant a period of 44 years of legal limbo for transexed people.

In the UK a Birth Certificate is the ultimate evidence of identity. Refusal to change it resulted in disclosure, invasion of privacy and denial of the right to marry, together with many ugly spin-off effects, which I explore here.

a) The Birth Certificate

is seen as an historical document, which could not be changed.

It placed the trans-person in a no man/woman's land.

By 1995 in all EEC Countries save the UK, Ireland and Austria; birth certificates could be changed post-operatively for a transperson. Even in the UK Certificates could be amended or re-announced in cases of obvious intersex. By 2002 only the UK, Albania and Ireland remained in Europe as non-congruent with this need to address the trans problem.

A new copy of your Certificate would be issued if, say you were a Dutch citizen living in England, or if you are British by birth, after application for Dutch Nationality, living in the Netherlands!

Perhaps we can now say that your place of birth, or your nationality was a determining factor in establishing your sex/gender! In Scotland, if births are registered in Scotland, it was possible to get a new certificate in some special cases, although this has been denied by officialdom. In the United Kingdom a birth certificate is deemed to be a statement of historical fact and record, which can only be altered if it was deemed to be false at the time of issue.

European law did in fact alter this situation eventually, because English Law did leave a large number of human rights issues for the TS, which seem to depend on the country in which a citizen lives. Of course the British are subjects, not citizens. We do not have a Bill of Rights or a Constitution only a branch of Law termed "Constitutional Law". The Magna Carta never took into account these complexities. But that is another debate!

In the British Courts, the Corbett Case effectively straightjacketed all TS's to their "biological sex", which was therein defined by chromosomes and original birth certificate!

b) Marriage.

As a result of *Corbett vs. Corbett (1970)* in which the marriage of April Ashley was deemed to have been null and void. (a case which was heard eventually before the House of Lords.) The consequence is that transexed women or men simply could not regard any marriage in GB as valid. (Tested also in *Peterson vs. Peterson 1985*).

They also found that an offence may have been committed under the Perjury Act 1911. The anomalous situation is that, based on a chromosomal definition of sex, a post-op MtF could marry a woman. However having no ability in law to consummate, the result would be void also presumably. However we look at the situation, a basic human right was denied the TS, and his or her partner in Great Britain.

c) Rape.

In *R v Tan 1983* it was held that, notwithstanding a sex change, a person born male remained "a man" for the purposes of the Sexual Offences Act. So MtF TS's could not say in law that they had been raped whatever happened to them. That meant the only option left was to charge an attacker with indecent assault, which related to both men and women. Imagine the horror of going before the Courts after such a trauma.

However the Criminal Justice and Public Order Act (1994) replaced the word "woman", when defining the victim, by "woman or another man." This has been replaced in turn by the Sexual Offences Act 2003 in which Rape is now classified as penetration of *anybody's* vagina, anus or mouth, without their consent, regardless of their sex or gender.

Clearly, though anyone can be a victim of rape, only a man, that is to say someone with a penis, can commit the offence. However it is now also an offence to penetrate the anus or vagina of someone else with sexual intent, and without consent, using any part of the body or with an object, such as, for instance, a dildo. This is defined as Assault by Penetration.

It remains to be seen what sentences the courts impose if the victim was transexed.

d) Pensions.

In many EEC countries pensions are paid to men and women at different ages - though not in all cases. At this time (2004) men receive their state retirement pension at 65 and women at 60, though some years hence, both men and women will not get their State Pension until they are 65.

e) National Insurance.

A National Insurance Number remains unchanged (post operatively etc.) - and so embarrassing difficulties may well occur. 'Early Retirement' may be one way out of this. The DSS has also ruled that a woman 'married' to a F to M TS cannot qualify for a Wife's retirement pension based on her transsexed partner's contributions.

There can be problems if a claim is thought to have been made fraudulently, with resulting non-payment of benefit, if there has been absolutely no revelation of the 'real story'. A birth certificate is sometimes requested as well as death certificate. A rule of thumb is to be honest with a senior company officer and ask for a private file with confidentiality assured. This will avoid the pitfall of a cry of 'deception'.

f) Divorce.

These days it need not involve a spouse divorcing a TS on the grounds of 'cruelty' or 'unreasonable behaviour', since the law now does allow less unpleasant grounds for divorce. In the past TS's could be divorced just because they were transexed or 'cross-dressers'. It does seem strange that the TS was in a way 'not allowed' to 'stay married', or to 'get married'.

g) Maintenance.

Ludicrous situations like a post-operative TS (MtF) ex-husband, who is a now a woman, has to maintain another woman (the ex-wife). A variation of Maintenance Order could adjust this to a more equitable situation if the ex-husband's financial state has altered drastically. However, in some circumstances the new woman might apply for maintenance for her ex-wife. One wonders just where this untidy mess of litigating oddities might end?

h) The anomaly of Testicular Feminization.

This anomaly has also not been addressed, demonstrating a lack of justice in law as it is. The 'girl' born with testicular feminisation has male chromosomes (XY) but externally 'looks female', is given a birth certificate saying 'girl'. She can marry, can't give birth, and can't have vaginal sex unless a vagina is surgically created. She can marry a man, and can retire at 60 on a state pension. Yes, 'the law is an ass' as Dickens so eloquently says. If law wished to espouse natural justice, it was obvious that it had to address the plight of transpeople.

i) Offences during change over (or even after surgery).

There are specific public order offences, which might still cause problems relating to prosecution of a 'male person masquerading as a female'. It is not illegal to dress in the clothes of the 'other gender'. Under Common Law a charge of Breach of the Peace could be made.

A charge could be (and has been) brought by a Police Officer following an arrest for conduct likely to cause a breach of the peace. The offender could be 'bound over to keep the peace' or fined on subsequent 'offences'.

The Sexual Offences Act 1956 (Sect. 32) might be applied if the (unthinking) MtF TS were out in a place of prostitution, or if they are seen waiting around dressed provocatively. The Act states that it is an offence for a man persistently to solicit or importune in a public place for immoral purposes (this includes public houses, but not clubs).

Trial by jury might be claimed for this offence if things get that far. Normally at least two Written Warnings are required before a prosecution is commenced. Initially a police officer may arrest you assuming you are a woman and you would be charged with soliciting. Get a good solicitor! Behave sensibly is our advice and avoid these problems.

The Public Order Act 1936 (sects 5 & 7).

Section 5 reads: *"It will be a summary offence for any person in a public place or any public meeting (a) to use threatening, abusive or insulting words or behaviour, or (b) to distribute or display any writing, sign or visible representation which is threatening, abusive or insulting with intent to provide a breach of the peace or whereby a breach of the peace is likely to be occasioned."*

A complaint has to be made by a person to a police officer. It is a difficult offence to disprove. It is a summary offence so will be dealt with by a magistrate's court and is unlikely to result in a prison sentence. Under the GR Act this should change. Trans people now have rights. The police may not harass them, nor may the public.

138

j) Sex Discrimination Act.

Equal opportunities - see under 'employment' law on the Press for Change and Gendys websites *http://www.pfc.org.uk* and *http://www.gender.org.uk/gendys/*

k) Prison.

Should a TS be sent to prison - they could (if preoperative and convicted) - be sent to the prison of their original gender type.

This happened even if hormonal reassignment and name change had taken place. The prison doctor or governor may refuse to allow hormone treatment to continue.

A post operative woman (MtF) could be treated the same and charged as in one case (1984) with living off immoral earnings (her own) but sent to a female prison. The Howard League takes an interest in prison reform and the various plights of prisoners. The best plan is to not be sent to prison, by flouting the law, or by behaving stupidly. After my, and others', liaison with Prison Governors and arising from the new Act, with the Prison Service special provisions are now mandatory, even including allowing gender treatment to continue.

64. Since the Gerbil the Birth Certificate can be Amended in the U.K.

Gender Recognition Act 2004.

The Third Reading of the Gerbil in the House of Commons was on May 24th 2004. When the House divided: Ayes 355, Noes 46 - So it was passed by an 87% majority. The Act was passed by the Lords and now has Royal Assent so it is Law. Transexed people will be able to marry in their acquired gender as part of new legislation to protect their basic human rights.

The effect of this Act will reverberate through the legal mess and hopefully the anomalies mentioned in the previous chapter will be removed.

The Gender Recognition Act gives legal recognition in their acquired gender to transexed people who can demonstrate that they have taken decisive steps towards living fully and permanently in their acquired gender, as opposed to the gender in which they were registered at birth.

In practical terms, it will mean that, for example, a male to female TS person will be legally recognised as a woman in UK law.

An authorising body will look at applications. It will have legal powers to assess medical evidence before the transsexual person is allowed to register in the new gender.

Successful applicants will be entitled to a new birth certificate that reflects their acquired gender.

During the debate the Minister at the Department for Constitutional Affairs, Lord Filkin said: *"I believe that the Gender Recognition Bill is farsighted. It honours the Government's commitment to guarantee the rights of transsexual people and brings us into line with the overwhelming majority of our European partners. It establishes a robust and authoritative process that will sustain a credible system for the future giving transsexual people the legal recognition to which they are entitled."*

The Department for Constitutional Affairs (DCA) will be implementing The Act.

The DCA are assessing the Gender Recognition process to ensure that it works as efficiently as possible. In particular, they have been mapping out how the applications are processed to see where potential delays in the system may occur due to a backlog of applications building up at any stage in the process.

To get the Act passed involved a lot of work from a great many people, some from PFC, some brave individuals going through the European and UK Courts, others from various support groups and consultative bodies. There has also been a good deal of liaison with Group representatives on Health Provision, Policing, Unions and so on.

Things have really improved now.

Probably if we had sought to please all the people so affected the Act might never have passed. There will still be a great deal to do implementing it, special cases, Care Standards and Provision, Equality issues, Training, Dealing with the Media, Research, Health issues and dealing with the bigots.

65. **Press For Change** - PFC - Is the small group of Rights campaigners who have done a great deal to lobby and so on, to change the Birth Certificate issue and promote the Gender Recognition Act. As the Act is (probably rather slowly) being implemented, various other issues will emerge. Keep up to date by using their (voluntary personnel)

e-mail news updates and projects. As usual they have received a lot of flak from some people - unanswered letters, no thanks for donations, high handedness (probably justified), but remember they are about twelve volunteers doing their best. You can not please everyone.

For those with access to the Internet, Press for Change operates a news service and on-line archive, UKPFC-NEWS, which provides up to date information about issues which affect trans people, including changes in the legal and bureaucratic process. This can be found at *http://www.pfc.org.uk/pfclists/* One cannot post to it, but items of interest may be sent to *news.intake@pfc.org.uk*. It should be noted that some material may be written by third parties, which is distributed for information only and may not reflect the views or policies of Press For Change. The postal address is BM NETWORK, London, WC1N 3XX.

66.   Identity Cards.
The issue of Identity Cards has not yet been decided in the UK, so it would be premature to discuss them at this point. Hopefully they should, if instituted, not be transparent in identifying a trans history for T people.

67.   Civil Partnerships.
This is a proposal yet to be resolved in the U.K.

It has relevance for gay or lesbian partners and for marriages in which a T person wishes to retain legal connection with her or his ex-spouse.

68   The Gender Recognition Act.
It is too early to describe the process which will be installed to deal with applicants for a new Birth Certificate, but the Act seems to ensure confidentiality and full legal rights in the newly recognised gender. As things develop a new Chapter will need to be installed here. Meanwhile keep abreast of this issue via PFC, support Group publications Gendys Journal and the Websites: *http://www.gender.org.uk/gendys/* and *http://www.pfc.org.uk/*

69.   Over 50's Survey.

A Survey of 60 Trans People Aged Fifty - Plus.

Researchers: Alice Purnell BSc RGN, PGDC., Dorothy Jerrome PhD, PGDC
Project 1995/6, Revised 2004

INTRODUCTION

To understand the experience of the over fifty year old (at the time of this survey in 1995) gender dysphoric people, it was necessary to place this cohort in its historical and social context. There had been important changes over the lifetimes of the people in the study, on a number of fronts: surgical, medical, legal, cultural and social.

In medicine different schools of thought have emerged in relation to the causes of gender dysphoria. They had moved from a clinical 'need to cure' towards a more pragmatic need to manage.

There had been a considerable debate between genetic and psychological aetiologies, between developmentalists and behaviourists and over a nature versus nurture causation.

Treatment over recent years became more individualised, leading to a wider range of treatment options ruled by pragmatic considerations.

The social support system expanded considerably, both in terms of formal organisations (GENDYS, Beaumont Trust, Gender Trust, FtM Network, Beaumont Society and informal networks and information and resources available.

On the cultural front, ideas about sex and gender had developed. Variations in sexual preference and alternative ways of expressing sexual needs had become more acceptable. Personal accounts of so called 'sex change' became publicly available in the form of celebrated autobiographies and mass media coverage. There is more scope for personal development along unique pathways.

Ideas about development over the life course have shifted: there are now more options, there is more flexibility and the importance of personal fulfilment is recognised. We considered each of these areas.

GROWTH OF INFORMATION - BACKGROUND

Prior to the mid 1960's there was little or no practical help for those who were gender dysphoric. Gender Dysphoria is a situation, which has practical, social, legal, medical and sometimes surgical solutions and implications. It has largely been in the control of psychiatrists, psychologists and surgeons although it is a phenomenon of individual identity. It presents challenges to the accepted norms of a society, which is bipolar in terms of its concepts of sex and gender and sexual preference.

Transsexualism was a term first suggested by Harry Benjamin in 1954, and only publicised in 1966 in his book *The Transsexual Phenomenon*. Prior to that year very few psychiatrists, surgeons and medics, and more particularly, society as a whole, were able to see the wood for the trees, in terms of gender identity conflict. Transsexualism first appears in the *Index Medicum* in 1969, and it was not until 1980 that the diagnostic criteria appeared in the D.S.M.

Sufferers were isolated, treated by the caring professions as mad, bad, or at best weird. Eccentricity is permissible in some spheres, but society demands conformity. Science created labels and people were to somehow conform to them. Thus there was a need to find a cure for what was seen as a sexual perversion, a form of sexual deviation. These people were, after all, seen as perverts, inverts or deviants.

Homosexuality was treated in much the same way until Professor John Money and others had it removed from the U.S. D.S.M. as a perversion, and its decriminalisation has progressed thanks to Stonewall and other civil liberties action groups. Great strides have been made following the new political awareness, pride and action to challenge legal systems, which were punitive rather than humanistic, not only towards women, people of colour and gays. The civil liberties battle in the Gay Rights movement in the U.S.A. and elsewhere have made a difference to people who are seen as 'different' and outsiders. This has meant that there has been a significant increase in openness in information and clear thinking in the seventies and onwards.

PSYCHOLOGICAL CONTEXT

There is a history of improving knowledge through scientific, sociological, anthropological and humanistic research and thinking and publications, which has slowly brought about the recognition of gender identity as an issue. This is bringing a consequent increased public awareness to a public, which now, as always, includes many of those suffering from gender dysphoria.

This means that those who are transexed, and transgendered people, indeed all who have had any kind of gender dysphoria, were simply not informed, for neither were the experts, prior to 1966. Many professionals in mental health still seemed to look only to Freud (1897 -1940) and his writings on psychoanalytic theory for an answer. Freud did not have or use a language to include gender identity.

He presents us with his final typology of the instincts (1921 & 1930) into *Eros* (life instincts) and *Thanatos* (death instincts), with culture and society as the outcome of the cosmic struggle between these two, assisted by *Ananke* (necessity).

But what of the hermaphrodite, what of the transexed person? How do they fit?

What Freud terms bisexuality includes all gender confusions as well as sexual preferences. It makes the mistake, still so often made, that is, to confuse cross-gender behaviour with homosexuality. This meant that anything that crossed the strict heterocentric rules of sex, sexual preference or gender was seen as a perversion, and probably mother's fault.

Krafft Ebing 1931 in his *Psychopathia Sexualis* with his forensic approach to what he terms a sexual inversion continues this hegemony. The same rigid patriarchal philosophy continues in Havelock Ellis in *Studies in the Psychology of Sex*, 1936, with his term *Eonism* as a form of sexual deviation.

Magnus Hirschfeld, in *Sexual Anomalies and Perversions* 1938, saw transsexualism as a deflection of the sexual impulse.

In Stoller, 1975, *The Transsexual Experiment*, there is still a theoretical stance, which suggests Transsexuality, is a form of homosexuality, the driver towards so called sex-change being a want of what was originally a same sex partner.

Although we owe a debt to Harry Benjamin (an endocrinologist) for providing a label to distinguish a group from another, the term itself is flawed, "Trans-sexual" suggests it is about sex, not gender identity.

Dr. Dorothy Clare introduced the term *transhomosexual* to cover those gender dysphoric people who felt a same sex preference in their resolved or imagined gender role. Brian Tulley and Dr. Clare enlarged the scope of this definition to include those who are not gender dysphoric, but who, none the less, have a fantasy of being homosexuals of the opposite sex.

**To escape the link with sexuality these days (2004) there is much debate about the terminology, many people preferring the term transexed to transsexual.

Yet there were still psychologists and psychiatrists who apparently could not see that so-called transsexuals were as likely as the rest of us to be either heterosexual, lesbian, homosexual, bisexual or asexual, irrespective of their gender identity. Sexuality is not the same as gender.

Sex, Gender, and sexual preference are all mutable, are variables along a spectrum of natural presentations.

Dr. Richard Green's study of "sissy-boys" showed that the majority of boys in his study became effeminate homosexuals as adults, rather than transsexual, so childhood indications are confusing.

It became necessary for some clinicians to differentiate between so called *True* or *Primary* Transsexuals, and *Secondary* Transsexuals.

The Primary Transsexual presented younger and probably had a less established identity in their gender at birth. They had a better prognosis and were less complex. One would expect follow-up studies to find that someone in their fifties who had muddled on, often with considerable success, as 'ordinary' men or women, who got married, had children, succeeded in work as men or women, who were transexed would fail. They had a great deal to lose in changing over, and much to learn and unlearn. They would have a more difficult life path and worse prognosis than those who had been helped early in life would.

So do their gains outweigh their losses?

The idea of early onset and presentation, versus late onset and presentation, was introduced to help to differentiate between the two groups postulated. Some professionals in the field appeared to forget that date of presentation before a psychiatrist is not the same as date of onset. There may have been a gap of many years; even half a lifetime before time made it impossible to mask this distress. Also there was no diagnosis or facility to recognise or treat this anomaly prior to the mid 1960's, so what could a person do about it?

The original philosophy of psychiatric care of gender dysphoric people, who were presumed to be mentally ill, was to try to cure them by various therapies. It was presumed that a physically healthy male had to be barking mad to convince himself that he was a woman, one of the 'weaker sex' in which women are seen as somehow lesser beings.

145

That he wished to be mutilated to facilitate this delusion only compounded the belief that he was definitely crazy. Crude and cruel attempts at a cure were made to cure them of this 'delusion'. No aversion or other therapy or medication has ever provided such a cure. It would now seem that gender identity is a fundamental aspect of identity. Prior to 1966 what help was available and how suitable was it?

People in their fifties (by 1990) were in their twenties or older when a breakthrough came about. It wasn't universal. The G.I.C. (Gender Identity Clinic) at Charing Cross Hospital was only starting up, then under the harsh regime of Dr. John Randall.

In the wider world there was no sudden switch in medical, psychological or public awareness of gender dysphoria. There were neither massive retraining schemes for psychiatrists, nor a movement in public awareness in the sixties. (Forty years later things are only slightly better).

It was not a glamorous area of medicine, indeed practitioners, especially surgeons, were at risk of being ostracised by their peers and exposed by the Press. It was seen as kinky, weird, strange. What was not realised was how great the suicide rate was among trans people and how much misery and isolation they felt.

The Unit at Charing Cross Hospital London has treated the lion's share of gender dysphoric people seen in the N.H.S. (About 6,000 patients by 1990). There are smaller gender identity units around the country. Patients knew a particular script would get results from the G.I.C.'s so they often lied to their psychiatrists. Hopefully now they can all get real.

Since this Unit is the centre of activity in this field it is important that it be also a centre of excellence. There has been much criticism of this unit by those it treated and those it could not help and rejected. The psychiatrist's role became that of Gatekeeper. Those who did not fit the "Standard transsexual pattern" were not helped in any way, save to deflect them from surgery. In some cases this was justified, but others needed help in coming to terms with what sort of trans person and who they were.

The lack of research also is a cause for concern.

Then there was the private sector to consider. There have been some surgeons who can only be described as butchers, others who failed to

146

have their patients screened by psychologists or psychiatrists and offered a snip on demand if the money was good.

There should be no hierarchy amongst gender dysphoric people, simply appropriate solutions for individuals. There are many questions arising from standards of care, ethical and practical matters to consider and the clinician's task is not an easy one, but surely a worthwhile one.

There were also pioneers who did wonderful work and rescued so many from a miserable existence.

Only with the beginnings of gender studies in the late seventies and eighties did women gain a voice, which sounded in the minds of a largely male dominated academia, medicine and finally the Media. Transexed people have followed their sisters in claiming recognition as individuals. This is now percolating into the largely male dominated world of psychiatry. Public opinion also seems to be shifting to a less hostile view.

It is only in keeping abreast of modern and more enlightened and informed thinking, can we get a clear picture of the differences between sex and gender drivers, in the development of an individual personality. We need to use a language that clearly defines its terms (as Prof. John Money insisted, whatever his faults, he is right here). Differences in the meanings of the words used and assumptions and errors of thought occurred. This was not only in the consciousness of the general public, or the client group, but among many professionals who had charge of their care.

SURGICAL AND MEDICAL CONTEXT

Great advances in reconstructive surgery has meant that it is possible with the aid of appropriate hormones to bring body and mind so much more into accord. Surgery is not always the appropriate solution for all gender dysphoric people. Reconstructive surgery has improved considerably in terms of vaginoplasty, clitoroplasty, colovaginoplasty, the cosmetic operation, mammectomy - retaining the nipples, and phalloplasty.

Nevertheless, a single-stage phalloplasty, which not only allows a new man to stand to void, but to be able to have sensation and a means of erection is some way off. This means most FtM's regard 'full surgery' as mammectomy and hysterectomy only, as their best option.

The involvement of endocrinologists and use of hormones is more refined and versatile, however the reversal of already established secondary sexual characteristics is not yet possible.

**In this century use of medication to delay puberty is being used in some juvenile cases.

Secondary sexual characteristics such as facial hair, deep voice and male pattern baldness in MtF people are a very real problem. This is why many MtF's spend more money on electrolysis or Laser treatments than on surgery, and things like a deep voice are constraints in entirely achieving a goal of perfectly acceptable womanhood.

Androgenisation is not reversible so there must be cautions in use of androgenic hormones on a FtM patient unless there is reasonable confidence that it is fully appropriate and safe for him.

None of the drug companies have completed (or even started) longitudinal studies on the long-term effects on this group of patients in terms of side-effects or complications. Thus there is a risk for both patient and the prescriber in the use of 'cross-sex' hormones, or of the effects of being agonadal once testes or ovaries are removed in this context, with or without hormone treatment continuing post surgery.

Advances in what is possible surgically and in the use of hormones are great, but sadly the man or woman with a transsexual background will probably never be able to function entirely normally in terms of the ability to have or to make children.

Better Phalloplasty surgery is now available for some FtM people, and Clitoroplasty seems to have improved the lot of the MtF person.

Medicine and surgery are advancing, so it would seem that if a person had to be born transexed, it would be better now rather than 50 plus years ago.

CULTURAL AND MEDIA CONTEXT

In Denmark, Lili Elbe had the first recorded surgical attempt at so called "sex change" in 1922. In her biography *Man into Woman* she explains her joy at the outcome, although it led to her death because of tissue rejection of the ovarian transplants.

The case of Christine Jorgensen was widely publicised in the U.S.A. and Europe. She was one of Benjamin's patients, and her case was the first of so many to receive media attention, generally of the sensationalist and unsympathetic sort. But at least it showed that something was possible to alleviate acute gender dysphoria.

In the U.K. the stories of Roberta Cowell, April Ashley, Michael Dillon, Mark Rees, Caroline Cossey, Jan Morris, Julia Grant and many others have acted so as to inform the public of this phenomenon, which sadly was regarded as something of a dirty joke.

Increasingly newspapers, save the gutter press, are featuring these problems reasonably well. Television programmes, like Oliver Morse's excellent coverage of adolescent FtM transsexuals in *Decisions* earlier in 1996, are gaining public sympathy and awareness of gender dysphoria.

It is significant, however, that the programme excluded MtF's (a more numerous group), perhaps in deference to lingering sexist attitudes in the Media.

SOCIAL NETWORKS.

Before the mid-sixties most gender dysphoric people were secretive or solitary, as invisible as possible. They felt they were unique and alone with their problem. The more outgoing involved themselves peripherally with the gay scene, drag clubs, and were open to blackmail and ridicule. It was to the mutual disadvantage of both as groups who in the public mind were identified as one 'type'. The antipathy towards gay men as "effeminate queers" and lesbians as "bull dykes", worked to the disadvantage of gender dysphoric people. They also became victims of homophobia just as the gays had always been victims of stereotyping.

SELF-HELP GROUPS

In the U.K. the first national organisation for gender-motivated transsexuals and transvestites was the Beaumont Society (1966). In 1975 the Beaumont Trust was formed as a registered charity, to provide help and information and was complementary to the function of the Beaumont Society, whose mandate was more one of networking and friendship. In 1983 Judy Cousins founded S.H.A.F.T., the first national self-help group specifically for transexed people. This evolved into the Gender Trust, and its membership group GEMS was founded (1990). The GENDYS Network was also founded in 1997 by this author. The FTM Network started in 1991. There are and have been many other national and local support groups and organisations in the U.K. for either TV's, TG's or TS's such as already mentioned and Transessex, Northern Concord, and Seahorse.

**Transvestites now prefer the term Cross-Dressers.

North America has a plethora of groups and organisations, and most countries in the English speaking world and the European Union have small local groups. However, Latin America, Eastern Europe and other areas in the world have no such national groups. Despite the growth of voluntary helping organisations those who are aware of the available groups represent only the tip of the iceberg. In the U.K, groups like GENDYS Network, GT, Beaumont Trust and the FTM Network, offer a range of services and information, but they have only relatively recently been formed. It is hardly surprising therefore that those born before the sixties had little or no appropriate help from anyone.

Younger TS's have been more fortunate. The emergence of a Gender Identity Unit for adolescent gender dysphoria sufferers in the Netherlands, then the Portman Clinic in London, in the same year as this Survey (1996), led to the formation of Mermaids - a group to help parents of children with gender identity problems. This demonstrates how far we have come in the last thirty years.

LEGAL CONTEXT

Although it is not illegal to be gender dysphoric it might as well have been in the United Kingdom since the case of April Ashley. There was a paradox in having a N.H.S. which provided help, yet laws, which still denied basic human rights in Great Britain. Press for Change with many others, worked hard, together with legal and medical experts, to effect changes more in line with the civil liberties one might hope for from an enlightened society. (See the Gerbil (2003) and the Gender Recognition Act 2004).

Even post-operatively the "Transexed" as men and women were marginalized and suffered real discrimination. At the time of the Survey the legal fact that birth certificates were not amended, thanks to the April Ashley Case, meant that a wide reaching series of legal inequalities resulted. This included making marriage post-op void or illegal, save to a woman. Also a woman whose Birth Certificate still stated "boy" was legally male (but is socially a woman). This resulted in many pitfalls and complexities in respect of her confidentiality and legal status. She could only marry a man, by committing perjury, and this union could not legally be consummated. She could marry another woman though. We know of at least 6 lesbian couples who have taken advantage of this anomaly.

Retirement and Pensionable age is still tied to the birth certificate, so the post-op woman in this age group was to get her pension at 65, not at 60 like other women. This in itself was a cause of outing for those who were employed, as are the unchanged National Insurance details.

LIFE COURSE DEVELOPMENT

In some ways, recognising one's gender dysphoria has become easier. Psychological theories of change over the life-course have become more enlightened, from the older adult's point of view. From earlier models of life-course development, which placed the emphasis on childhood and early experience, we are now open to the possibility of growth and change in the second half of life. Such theorists as Erikson and Jung express the new humanistic emphasis on adult development, on personal fulfilment and integrity.

In America, social Gerontologists concerned with the quality of adult life have emphasised the importance of achieving our personal potential (though the definition of what that is might change as we acquire life experience), of becoming more fully human as we grow older. In this perspective, ageing is a process of becoming more the person you really are. "Growing older" is about GROWING, rather than decline and loss. With critical attention being turned to the nature of the ageing experience, gerontologists have become more discriminating about the phases of adult life. We recognise new categories and sub-categories: mid-life, late middle age, old age, deep old age, and so on. Each of these has their own developmental tasks and goals.

Mid-life is seen as a time of change and growth: rather than the beginning of the end it is the end of the beginning. An awareness of mid-life potentials releases many adults from the need to conform to oppressive social requirements and outdated personal goals. The models of ageing in academic psychology parallel those in popular culture expressed in the media, which emphasise self-awareness, the need for personal fulfilment and increasing individualism. The liberation movements of the 1960's 70's and 80's expressed the same notion of personal rights to self-fulfilment. The gender movement, and gender dysphoria groups within it, was part of this larger, cultural trend.

In short, ideas about the life course have changed, affecting the way individuals see themselves moving through time.

151

METHODOLOGY

We looked at a range of gender dysphoric people and how they were resolving their life-long problems.

The study group was all over 50 years old at the time of the survey (1996).

We sent out 150 survey forms to members of GT/GEMS, FTM, and some Beaumont Society people who belong to the over 50's group. **There were 60 replies.**

We also interviewed some people in depth, held one group meeting and various telephone conversations with our sample of people, so that the content of this project is both quantitative and qualitative.

The aim of the group discussions was to expand on the questionnaire, capturing the uniqueness of experience, but also the collective experience of a particular cohort. We were looking for a sense of what it was like to be a gender dysphoric child in the 1930's and 1940's, or a teenager in the 1950's.

We supposed that as young adults the elderly TS's had faced difficult decisions - to marry or not to marry, to become a parent or not - at a time when social pressures to conform were stronger. We also wondered about the impact of changing concepts of femininity and masculinity over the century. We were concerned with ideas about age-appropriate styles of dress and behaviour over a person's life course, and wondered how older MtF's responded to the pressure to "be their age" when they had missed out on the fun years of girlhood and young womanhood.

We imagined the study would raise as many questions as answers.

SURVEY FINDINGS

The purpose of our survey was to examine older TS's both as a group and as sub groups and individuals.

We interviewed several subjects, and all completed a questionnaire. Those who replied included women (post-op MtF) TS's, men (post-op FtM) TS's, pre-operative Transexed people, Transgenderists (who have not opted for surgery, but are living in role) and Transvestites (Cross-dressers).

(Apologies for not repeating the better term "Transexed Person")

The 61 who completed the questionnaires in whole or in part were invited to classify themselves, and did so as follows:

FtM = 8, of whom 5 are post-op men, 3 were pre-op.

MtF = 53, 43 said they were transsexual, 28 were pre-op and 14 are post-op women.

2 were born intersexed, there were also 2 transvestites,

7 transgenderists (not opting for surgery).

Interestingly a number who may in the past have described themselves as full or part-time TV's now use the expression transgenderist. The transvestites described themselves as content in either role, as interestingly did 10% pre-op TS's. We have assessed the answers collectively in various ways, to make comparisons.

AGE

To place this group in context, they include middle age and elderly. Half have lost their mother, 70% their father is dead, 50% have lost both parents, 10% have no surviving siblings, 58% were aged 50 to 60; 27% were over 60; and 15% were over 70.

.		Range	Average
Age	MtF	50 yrs - 85yrs	60yrs
	FtM	51 yrs - 75yrs	57yrs
Height	MtF	63" - 75"	68"
	FtM	60" - 67"	64"
Weight	MtF	133lb - 206lb	160lb
	FtM	109lb - 149lb	130lb

Conclusions: from these respondents the MtF's are on average 4" taller and 30lb heavier than the FtM's. Height can be an issue, and weight is also a problem for some MtF's. Height and weight are influenced by sex at birth and there is little to suggest a particular body frame accords with a gender dysphoric identity.

Observation from interviews: Size of hands and feet and other physical attributes can be a problem for some individuals in terms of 'passing' i.e. being within the range of the physical norms expected by others in respect of apparent gender. As we know voice can also be a problem for some MtF's.

The older 'trans' person does sometimes have age on his or her side, since secondary sexual characteristics are to an extent camouflaged by

153

the effects of ageing. Voice pitch often goes up in old age in males and down in females, body hair diminishes as hormones have less effect, hair becomes grey and finer in many cases. Since male-pattern baldness often happens to FtM's this helps them, but in the MtF's this can necessitate a wig.

The fact is a little old man can be a reasonably convincing little old lady, and vice-versa, if they are socialising according to age and gender norms. It seems even a little eccentricity is expected in England. It is harder for the middle-aged who are tempted to be mutton dressed as lamb, particularly if they never had a chance to be the right sort of lamb. Some people seem to find it difficult to adopt an age-appropriate style of dress, but some seem to be stylish by any standards. Perhaps the answer is as the poem goes "To wear purple"!

Fewer expectations are placed on older people in terms of sexual attractiveness in a youth-oriented society. As younger people do not see them as sex objects, they are not scrutinised so closely in public. Children look more closely and are less inhibited. They can be a problem to those who do not pass well. Within the elderly peer group, however, people can still be assessed in terms of their sexual attractiveness. However, this quality is not what elderly TS's seek, so much as acceptance in their real gender identity.

There are constraints against the older person presenting for surgery, which are as a direct result of having no effective help available prior to the mid-sixties. Many have had established lives, careers and jobs and more particularly a partner (usually a wife) and often children who they do not wish to hurt by embarking on anything irreversible.

The pressure to grow up in the gender role assigned at birth, to marry and produce children, and the gradual accumulation of irreversible family commitments, might account for the lapse of time between recognising a gender problem and acting on it. The lapse of time between awareness of gender dysphoria, going out 'dressed' in public, seeking professional help and finally making the transition was sometimes considerable.

The Group Discussion (joined by six MtF's and 2 FtM's) ranged widely over the experience of growing up and growing older, revealed some of the reasons for the delay. The general picture that emerged for the early years was one of repression, misunderstanding and stress-related illnesses. In the 1930's and 40's it was impossible to share

154

feelings with parents or the family doctor. In childhood and adolescence, thoughts of the opposite sex were likely to be described as "dirty", and like sex, not talked about. Sex education in the 1930's and 1940's at school and home was minimal. One young person's source of information was a booklet found in mother's drawer, *What Every Young Wife Needs to Know,* but 'she' could not talk to 'her' mother about it.

Negative attitudes on the one hand and a lack of knowledge on the other set the gender dysphoric child apart, alone and lonely. In the absence of role models such children did not know what they wanted, they only knew what they didn't want. The stigma attached to homosexuality, with which all sexual deviation was identified, was not encouraging. In their ignorance they assumed that their desires, like those of homosexuals, were illegal. They experienced years of secret longing and fantasies, more real in some ways than the spectres of unpleasant reality.

Someone said it was like being on a ghost train. This metaphor seems to sum up the experience of turbulence and terror, the real self in conflict with the unreal world.

In some ways the experience was different for boys and girls. There was pressure on boys to be masculine, and deviations from the norm were punished. In confusion, the affected children often joined in the censure of "queers, poofs and sissies". The sense of simultaneous revulsion and identification set up terrible conflicts.

Responses varied. Children who were verbally abused, beaten and punished for their unmasculine behaviour complained of a range of stress-related conditions - ulcers, stomach disorders, and depression. Others survived the ethos of the single-sex school by avoiding extra-curricular activities, sports, showers, army cadets, summer camps and shared dormitories.

It was somewhat easier to be FtM, with the general acceptance of tomboys and role models in children's literature (such as Enid Blyton's *George*). In the 1940's the land girls and other women doing men's work demanded a more liberal concept of femininity. But FtM's also felt very isolated, "the only one in the world".

There were no public role models until the naval doctor Michael Dillon's story appeared in the press. The MtF's were more fortunate in having Roberta Cowell (1954) and Christine Jorgensen (1965), and many

155

others as role models. Such people made it easier to resist the pressure to, for instance, join the army (to be turned into real men). In general there was no alternative to passing. Outward conformity was vital. In a sense there were no choices to be made, since there were no alternatives. Gender dysphoria was "something you just didn't talk about, you got on with your life". Strength was a feature of early life, at least for the survivors. "You had to stand alone", and those who were able to do so now feel super-strong.

For those people who completed the **Questionnaire,** the sense of dysphoria came very young (for more than a third of the respondents - 18/59 - it was present as early as 3, 4 or 5), and half were aware under 8 years old. However, some (6/59) were not aware and did not start cross-dressing (10/59) until mid-life or later, going out in public even later and seeking medical help at about the same time.

In detail, our Questionnaire findings were as follows:

When were you aware of a gender identity problem?							
	Age of awareness						
	Under 7,	8-15,	16-21,	21-30,	30-50,	50-65,	65+
FtM pre -op	2/2						
post-op	5/6	1/6					
MtF TV	2/2						
MtF No-op TS	4/8	1/8	1/8	1/8	1/8		
MtF No-op TG	4/7	1/7	2/7				
MtF Pre-op TS	10/22	3/22	1/22	2/22	2/22	2/22	1/22
MtF Post-op	7/14	4/14	2/14	1/14			

Not allowing for problems with recall of such early experience, it would seem that all the FtM's were aware of gender dysphoria in early childhood, although they could not know the term. The MtF's were on average slightly older before this realisation.

The post-op MtF's resembled the FtM's in their early recognition of the condition. For these transexed children the ages of 3, 4 and 5 this awareness appeared critical.

Given this early onset, it is interesting to note the pattern of cross-dressing. Just under half (24/59) did this consciously for the first time between the ages of 10 and 15.

This perhaps shows the ingenuity of later childhood and early adolescence.

Again, allowing for difficulties with recall, the FtM's were most likely to do this at an early age and the post-op MtF's is generally earlier than the TV's and TG's.

At What Age First Cross-dressed?							
	under 7,	8-15,	16-21,	21-30,	30-50,	50-65,	65+
FtM pre -op	2/2						
FtM post-op	3/6	1/6	1/6	1/6			
MtF TV	2/2						
MtF No-op TS	2/8	4/8	1/8				
MtF No-op TG	4/7	1/7	2/7				
MtF Pre op TS	6/22	11/22	2/22	1/22	1/22		1/22
MtF Post-op	4/14	7/14	1/14	1/14	1/14		

One self-diagnosed pre-op MtF transexed person did not start to cross-dress until aged 74.

There seems to be an older average age for public cross-dressing among the MtF's, which is fairly evenly distributed, with peaks before puberty and then in later mid-life, and also after 1990.

During that and subsequent years there was more media exposure and information available from networks.

All but 1 of the FtM's went 'out in public' as men, under 30 years of age. However 3/4 of the MtF's did not do so prior to 30 years old. The challenge of going out in public took longer to meet for the MtF's, because they are more fearful of the consequences. A surprisingly large number of respondents had only done this relatively recently, in their middle and later years. It is reasonable to ask whether this might be an expression of a mid-life crisis for some transgenderists.

At what Age did you first out in public as member of preferred gender?							
Years of age	under 20,	20-30,	30-40,	40-50,	50-60,	60-70,	70+
FtM	3/6	2/6	1/6				
MtF No op	2/7	1/7	4/7	1/7			
MtF Pre op	1/22	3/22	5/22	5/22	3/22	3/22	3/22
MtF Post op	1/14	4/14	4/14	2/14	2/14	1/14	

There did not seem to be a significant difference between pre-op and post-op people here.

If we look at the distribution over time, some interesting facts emerge.

The FtM's all went out in public almost as soon as they could, that is prior to 1955 (i.e., For the MtF's there was a bunching in the 1990's, with almost half (10/23) of respondents going out in public for the first time then).

This was part of an accelerating trend, for in 1995 alone, 5 people took the plunge. This suggests that people felt empowered by particular public events such as significant television programmes.

The gradual ground swell in favour of gender variation, and the build up of informal networks support groups and activities, must also be a contributory factor.

We also looked at awareness of gender dysphoria in terms of historical events, but the pattern was less distinct. Among the pre-op MtF's there was some bunching around the war and post-war years, 1939 to 1950 (19/23), but whether this was a reflection of age-related developments or historical events is not clear. Perhaps the upheavals of wartime Britain allowed people (on the Home Front at least) to imagine alternatives and break social and personal conventions, as fictional accounts such as *The Camomile Lawn*, by Mary Wesley, illustrate well. It would appear that this freeing up was not affected significantly by the establishment of the first Gender Identity Clinic in 1966, which made no difference to the study population, largely because few knew about it.

Given the early awareness of dysphoria, the years of cross-dressing and of anguish, the decision to seek professional help came relatively late. FtM's made earlier appeals for help.

The MtF's from this over 50's survey generally sought medical help in their 40's (14), 50's (20) and 60's-70's (8). Again, in terms of year, the 1990's have seen a burst of activity, with half of the group (24) seeking help in the last 5 years. In 1992 alone, 6 people approached the medical profession.

These findings bring the early onset - late onset debate to the forefront of our attention. In view of the evidence of early awareness but postponement of action, it becomes much harder to adopt a simple classification along the lines of early or late onset.

In terms of historical events, certain years stand out. Only 27% sought and received any sort of medical, hormonal, psychological intervention, or counselling before 1966 (when the Charing Cross G.I.C. was founded), half the FtM's. 30% of the respondents did so after 1990.

This is not surprising since this year the Gender Trust and FtM Network were formed. The effect of networks and self-help groups cannot be underestimated in providing information and helping people to come to terms and hopefully find their own solutions.

At what Age you First Sought Medical/Emotional Help?

		under 7	8-15	16-21	21-30	30-50	50-65	65+
FtM	pre-op	1/2	1/2					
	post-op	2/6	3/6	1/6				
MtF	TV	1/2						
MtF	No op TS	3/8						
MtF	No op TG	2/7	1/7	4/7				
MtF	Pre op TS	2/22	7/22	9/22	5/22			
MtF	Post op	1/14	1/14	6/14	6/14			

For whatever reason the TS delays his or her request for gender confirmation surgery, the clinician has his or her own view of the appropriateness of medical intervention.

The medical view has often appeared unsympathetic to the older TS. The view seems to be that the social adjustments, the increased surgical risks later in life, the lack of interest in sex expected later in life, the losses against the gains, mean a less satisfactory prognosis and outcome might result, if these older patients are treated.

Interestingly there have been no large longitudinal studies on the long-term effect of administration of 'opposite sex' hormones on patients who presented early in life. However the drive to recognise and get their Transsexuality treated seems to be equally strong among the older gender dysphoric people, in spite of all they might seem to be losing.

We quote "A few years as myself means that my whole life will not have been wasted, and unhappy".

Gender dysphoric people may become either martyrs or victims or tyrants in this sort of trap. Their loved ones often also often pay a price.

HORMONES.

One in four of the no-surgery group were not on female hormones, whilst 75% of the pre-op group were, and 15% of the post-op group were not. The FtM's were on male hormones, except two of the post-op men. Osteoporosis may be a problem for those who are agonadal and not taking anything to prevent this.

We asked those on Hormones has your sex drive?			
	Decreased	No Change	Increased
FtM Pre op	NIL	2/6	NIL
FtM Post op	NIL	3/6	1/6
MtF No op	NIL	4/15	NIL
MtF Pre op	14/19	4/19	1/19
MtF Post op	5/11	3/11	3/11

This dispels the myth that the FtM sex drive increases dramatically once on androgens. It would seem there is a boost, then it settles down.

Half the FtM's report that they have adequate body hair, 80% have good beard growth, 1/3 show male pattern balding, and 60% say they have satisfactory muscular development, all on androgens have an enlarged clitoris. One uses a device to pad his trousers to compensate for not having had a phalloplasty.

The MtF group seems less sexually active, as would be expected on anti-androgens and Oestrogens. About 60% of the pre-op MtF's report that their penis has atrophied, as an effect of the hormones.

20% of the MtF's employ padding or a prosthesis in their bra, but none post-op do, although 8/14 had breast implants, as did 2 pre-op's. This means 3/14 developed adequate busts on hormones alone post-op, as did 50% pre-op. Perhaps this indicates that once surgery takes place a bigger breast seems a good idea to some. A caution remains, that if they have implants at the time of surgery, occasionally the breasts get bigger still post-op, and this can be inconvenient. 60% of all those on Oestrogens said their breasts are pleasantly sensitive.

Asked about body hair, 8% are troubled by it. It does not dramatically reduce with hormones, but does so with ageing. 1/3 of the pre-op group use a wig or hairpiece, whilst 1/5 of the post-op's do. Although male beard does not reduce with hormones, unless taken pre-puberty, when beard growth may be retarded, re-growth is apparently reduced for those undergoing electrolysis whom are on Anti-androgens and Oestrogens.

Hormone Regimes Individuals in our group were on:

Hormones	Dose	Age	Years On.	Side Effects
Premarin	7.5mg	65	2 +	
Androcur	200mg	65	2	Flatulence
Estraderm		72	1	
+Dianate		72	1	
Premarin	1.25mg	52	1	
Estraderm Tts	50	55	1	
Premarin	7.5mg	50	2	
+ Provera	10.0	50	2	
Premarin	7.5mg	45	6 +	
Provera	10.0	45	6	Loss Body Hair Joint Pain
Premarin	2.5mg	52	4	
+Medroxyprogesterone		52	4	Brittle Nails. Dry Skin
Oestradiol Impts	30mg.	60	1	Mood Swings
Androcur	100mg	60	1	
Androcur	100mg	55	6	Breast Dev ?Pulmonary Embolism.
Premarin	Varied	55	9	Water Retn, Various Pains.
Premarin	0.625	71	4	
Then Premarin Inc.5mg			3	
+Progestrogen		71	3	
Stilboesterol		27		2 Yrs Post Op
Stilboesterol				Stopped After D.v.t.
Stilboesterol		39	22	30 Yrs Post-op
Then Premarin	1.25	67	2	
Stilboesterol		26	31	
Then Premarin	0.625mg	71	4	13 Yrs Post-op.
Stilboesterol		30	20	Sick..Stopped
Then Premarin	2.5mg			
+Provera	250			Depressed..Stopped
Then Ovran +Noresterone				
Premarin	7.5mg	60	8	14 Yrs Post -Op
+Provera	5mg	60	8	
Then Premarin	2.5mg	68	7	
+Provera	5mg	68	7	

Hormones	Dose	Age	Years On.	Side Effects
Premarin	7.5mg	55	1	Weight Gain
+ Androcur		55	1	Phlebitis
Then Otivan	2	56	1	
Then Oestradiol	5mcg	57	1	
Then Evotcel Patches		57	1	2x2 A Week, 1yr Post-op
Premarin	7.5mg	50	3	Headache, Dizziness
Androcur	150	50	3	Stomach Cramps
				Stopped Hormones
Premarin	5mg	47	4	
Premarin	5mg			Stopped After 2yrs= Angina At 60
Premarin	5mg	54	2	Bust Dev. Cramps
Premarin	7.5mg	57	3	
Premarin	7.5mg	40	20	14 Yrs Post-op
Premarin	7.5mg	52	3	
Then Premarin	2.5mg	55	3	2 Yrs Post-op
				Sun, Metal Allergies. Brittle Nails
Premarin	7.5mg	57	2	
Premarin	2.5mg	51	1	Water Retention
Premarin	0.25	59	6	
Premarin	7.5mg	46	6	
+Provera	10mg	46	6	
Premarin	5mg	55	6	Phlebitis. Itchiness
+Provera	10mg	55	6	
Premarin	5mg	71	4	Tiredness
Bendroflurazide	5mg	47	5	For Hypertension
Ethinoestradiol	100mcg	50	3	
Ethinoestradiol	100mcg	56	2	
Ethinoestradiol	100mcg	63	3	Headaches, Nosebleeds.
Then				
Ethinoestradiol	50mcg	63	3	5 Yrs Post-op
Ethinoestradiol	100mcg	57	3	Leg Cramps
Then Ovran	100mg	58	2	
+Zumenon	4mg	58	1	
Ethinoestradiol	100mcg	51	1	
Then Ovran	100mg	52	2	
+Drogenil	1250	52	1	Premenstrual Tension

Hormones	Dose	Age	Years On.	Side Effects
Ethinoestradiol	100mcg	47	5	
+ Androcur	100mg	47	5	
Ethinoestradiol	100mcg	47	3	3 Yrs Post-op
+ Duphaston	20mcg	47	3	
Then Duphaston		52	6	Weight Gain
Ethyloestradiol	100mcg	52	6	Brittle Nails
Then Estraderm		56	2	
+ Androcur		56	2	
Duphaston	20mcg	46	6	
Then Premarin	2.5mg		1	
Noresterone	10mg		1	
Ovran	X2	51	1	
Zumenon		50	1	
+Androcur		50	1	
Primostenin		32	20	
Sustanon	100	35	17	20 Yrs Post-op Swelling Round I/m Site
Sustanon	250 I/m	23	31	Intermittent Migraine
Sustanol	250 I/m	40	26	
Testosterol Sub/ling 100		51	24	9 Yrs Post-op Stopped Hormones Because of Cataracts
Methyl Testosterone		31	5	20 Yrs Post-op
Then Viromone I/m 100mg.		36	27	Eyes Inflamed Because of Methyl. Testos.
Methyl Testosterone		28	13	20 Yrs Post-op
Then Sustanon		42	12	Hypertension

NB i/m = intramuscular injection

s/c = subcutaneous - under the skin - injection.

Most 'male' hormones are not absorbed orally, they are destroyed by the acids in the stomach, so are injected.

Of the 61 people who completed the survey, 53 completed the questions on hormones.

It is fair to say no two people have absolutely identical hormone regimes here, or responses to particular substances.

To summarise the side effects reported by those on long term medications stated the following:

Sustanol:	Hypertension, Intermittent migraine, i/m site swollen
Methyl Testosterone:	Inflamed eyes
Testosterol:	Stopped because of Cataracts
Ethyloestradiol:	Brittle nails, Pre-menstrual Tension, Headaches, Nosebleeds, 2 had leg cramps
Duphaston:	Weight gain
Premarin:	Tiredness. Hot flushes. Phlebitis, Itchy skin, Sun allergy, Metal allergy, Weight gain, Brittle nails. Leg cramps, Various Pains, Water retention. Headache. Dizziness. Stopped Premarin because of Angina at 60.
Androcur:	Phlebitis, Pulmonary Embolus, Flatulence. Stomach Cramps
Stilboesterol:	Stopped after Deep Vein Thrombosis. Sickness ..stopped
Oestradiol:	Mood swings
Medroxyprogesterone Acetate (Provera)	
	Dry skin, Brittle nails, Depressed, Joint Pain, Loss of body hair

Whilst these are reported as side effects, they may in some cases be a reflection of the age, body type, smoking tobacco, alcohol abuse, lifestyle and other variables.

The sample was too small to be empirical, however trends demonstrate that there may be side effects. These are a cause for concern. Monitoring the person's health by their GP is important. The Hormone regime needs to be tailor-made for each person and may need to be changed with time.

There is a legal requirement for Drug Companies to publish Clinical Trial results. Licences are given once trials prove their therapeutic effectiveness and any side effects. A balance between risk and benefit is taken. No trials have been made on the long-term use of 'cross sex' hormones or any risk assessment published for this small group of people. There is obviously some risk to both prescriber and the person taking hormones - or not taking any for that matter.

It is vital that trans people do not self prescribe and get hormones on the Internet without any health checks. These are powerful drugs.

It is a waste of money to buy creams and pills sold by rip-off companies.

SURGERY

The earliest surgery reported in this study was one in 1966 and one in 1968, with half of the respondents having had surgical interventions in the last 6 years.

Of the 53 MtF's,

43 termed themselves as transsexual,

14 post-op, including 2 intersexed.

29 pre-op transsexual or t/g 9 are not opting for surgery; these are the 2 transvestites and the 7-transgenderist people (Who use this term as a label different to TV or pre-op TS).

The reasons for not opting for surgery are 1 Poor reaction to hormones, 1 Headaches, Dizziness, 1 Height, 1 Angina, 4 Because of family, 1 too traumatic, 2 Work, 1 Too late, 2 age. 3 Inability to pass in public, 1 Need more time.

Pre-operatively the difficulties expressed were: "I am neither one sex or the other" "I have no interest in physical sex" "I'm a man without genitalia," "I want to be complete" "Penile prosthesis is no good."

Operations Performed? Of the 14 post-op (MtF) women there were the following:

11 Vaginoplasty (6 in the last 6 years). 3 Clitoroplasty. 7 Breast implants, including 1 saline. 1 Orchidectomy 2 Cosmetic

1 vocal cords 1 Rhinoplasty. No Colo-vaginoplasty were reported in this survey There were 8 FtM's; all included themselves as transsexual. 6 were post-op men; two felt they needed further surgery. 6 mastectomies, 2 total hysterectomy, 2 partial hysterectomy 3 construction of a phallus. The remaining 2 were pre-op.

The average age at gender confirmation surgery of the group of MtF's was 50, with a range of 27 years old at surgery to 61, and years post-op is from 1 year to 26, with only 2 under 40 years old at the time of surgery.

Among the FtM's the **average age of mastectomy and hysterectomy** was 35, and years post-op 27. The break through year for surgery was 1968 MtF and 1966 FtM, with 3 of the MtF's before 1980 and 3 in the 1980 are the rest in the 1990's. Among the FtM's this entire sample had their first surgery in the 1970's.

The post-ops were asked if they had any difficulty with sexual relationships since surgery.

7/8 FtM said they did, listing their problems as: "My sex organs", "I never sought sexual contact", "I was not given the chance to try", "Problems with the penile prosthesis, very frustrating".

The answer is a fairly clear "YES" for the FtM's.

Further comments were, "I'm a man with no genitals", and another says "I have no genitals."

Interview of FtM people seems to indicate that the main drive towards surgery was to prevent hated periods, and equally hated breasts.

Many transexed people express dysmorphophobia = hatred of their body.

Since good Phalloplasty has not really been available until comparatively recently, and it is still not perfect, few opted for construction of a phallus. All would prefer to stand to urinate, like other men. If it were possible to get an erectile penis, indeed to ejaculate, fertilise and function perfectly sexually as a man, most would wish to do so. Sadly this is not yet possible.

So a post-op FtM man sees himself as such, even without the phallus, after all "a man is not his penis, but it helps", as one said.

All the 8 FtM's were living in role. The length of time they had been doing this varied from 15 to 34 years, although two had not had surgery.

The MtF's had generally been living in role for shorter periods. 28 of the 52 had been doing so for less than 10 years, whilst 2 had been living in role for 40 years as transgenderists who had decided against the surgical option.

It would seem many FtM's were living in their chosen roles much longer, despite the absence of full surgery, and had benefited from the effects of androgenisation by means of testosterone injections, on the voice, beard and superimposition of male secondary characteristics. Some were able to resolve their problems living as men in their twenties, even before support from the gender identity clinics became available. For most of their adult lives they have been able to pass, at least in public. In private the situation may be more problematic, without an acceptable set of functioning male genitals.

Gender Dysphoria is unusual in that the patient (I would prefer to say the individual client) has often reached the diagnosis her or himself and is sufficiently well motivated and informed that, apart from structural improvements (using hormones and surgery), she is alone responsible

166

for his or her own 'treatment'. That is to successfully cross this bipolar gender-divide.

The process of assessment by a psychiatrist is to assess the eligibility for his patient to receive what is termed "triadic therapy". This consists of real life experience, hormones and surgery.

There is a sense in which he, the psychiatrist, is placed in the role of god, providing salvation or hell. His cautions seem unreasonable to the convinced self-diagnosed person.

I believe that this results in each in being placed in conflicting positions, in what may better be seen as a co-operation towards seeking and reaching an appropriate resolution of these problems. In fact the psychiatrist is one of a team in which the client is the most important player.

Employment

The 8 FtM's are either self employed or retired, as is generally the case with the MtF's, although there is a wider range of employment options demonstrated in that group:

Retired 34%,	Retired / Students 4%,
Retired in voluntary work 8%,	Part-time work 2%,
Unemployed 6%,	Self-employed 24%,
Employed 16%,	Incapacity 2%.

The largest single group is retired in some way and constitutes half the MtF's. Many have taken early retirement, one saying she was forced into it. There is much evidence that this is a line taken by many employers. It is encouraging that 12% were students or in voluntary work as part of their 'real life test'. It would seem the self-employed found the changeover least stressful.

45% Told their employer (Which means 25% of those who work for someone else have not told them, i.e. some pre-op's work in 'original' gender role), and some post-op's have not told their employer of their history.

The sort of **_difficulties that arose_** are listed here:

"Some colleagues say that I'm a man," "I won't know how they will be until I'm full-time."

The majority of people in the survey were either retired or self-employed. Voluntary work or study are options which some take up to satisfy the requirements of the real-life-test.

Many have taken early retirement, one saying she was forced into it. There is evidence that this is a line taken by many employers. It would seem the self-employed found the changeover least stressful.

Self Evaluation of Quality of Life and Standard of Living

We asked about standard of living and quality of life. Not surprisingly there was no direct correlation between them.

Most of the MtF's had taken a drop in standard of living, as a result of breaks in employment, poorer pay, and other difficulties affecting material circumstances: divorce settlements, housing and so on.

Their quality of life, however, was seen in almost in all cases as having risen as a result of their gender confirmation, even for those who had not yet had surgery and those who decided against it. This was true for both MtF's and FtM's.

	Standard of Living			Quality of life		
	risen	no change	fallen	risen	no change	fallen
FtM	40%	40%	20%	25%	75%	nil
MtF	4%	60%	36%	86%	14%	nil

It would seem that the effects of gender identity on the quality of life might compensate for the drop in standard of living, though these changes are only relative and do not tell us about the magnitude of the changes, or their overall impact on life satisfaction. People seem to be saying they are much happier than before the changeover. All said that they were very happy or happier since surgery.

We asked if since changeover they felt they were more or less or the same in terms of **emotional success** 60% said "more" and 40% "the same". The same sort of figures were true socially, they felt better about themselves and more at ease.

They were asked about **life satisfaction,** and all but 6% said they we very happy or happier than before living full time in role, hormones, or surgery, where applicable.

We asked about **hobbies.** The FtM group had hobbies and interests, which seemed markedly masculine in gender stereotypical terms, before and after their changeover and surgery. The MtF's also started in the main, with traditional 'masculine' hobbies and interests, they often seem to swing into hyper-feminine activities, then settle down to a more liberated resumption of their wider scope of interests.

168

This gender specific movement seems most apparent in the pre-op MtF's, who seem to rush to take up knitting and dressmaking, only a year or two later, post-op do they feel able to fix the car, as do many other women of the nineties.

In fact 25% of the MtF's did change their hobbies and interests, although part of this is possibly a function of retirement, ageing and circumstances, as much as taste, or the 'official' consequences of change of gender role. It may be an advantage to be skilled in both roles in a society, which is blurring the gender stereotypes.

80% said they felt they were sociable or gregarious, whilst 14% said they were shy. 40% said this had changed since hormones, with comments like "I am more sociable, gregarious, extravert", and 1 "more shy".

About 60% of the post-ops said they had experienced a generally positive improvement in well being and confidence.

We asked about Stress?

It is a stressful time "living in the wrong gender" In the Group sessions and telephone interviews what came over was how stressful it is to be in the trans situation, especially before it was resolved.

The 'real-life-test' was found to be especially stressful, living as the right gender but feeling or looking intermediate, with the 'wrong body'. Whilst there was joy at progress towards harmony of mind and body and the positive effects of hormones, together with enhanced emotional responses often happening, there was the turmoil of changing relationships, loneliness, a second puberty, and self-doubts at 'passing' as preferred gender. There was also the hurtful ridicule or hostility of others and fear of media exposure.

We asked what was their Greatest Cause of Stress?

Most of those expressed were from pre-op people: I am stressed because:

"Most men put me off, sympathetic ones but not able to make love"

"No sexual relationships, though plenty of friends"

"I relate to females as a female, am I a lesbian?"

"I don't want sex with a man until I'm a woman"

"Fear of how it might affect our grandchildren"

"Being unable to express my female side"
"I have lost contact with my four children"
Three say, "Not being full-time"

"Coming out to close friends"	"No live-in partner now"
"Occasional panic attacks"	"Great internal tension"
"The medical profession"	"Being two people"
"Being incomplete"	"Loneliness"
"Nothing"	"Deceit"

Caring Relationships?

All but 25% FtM and 6% MtF sample who replied reported that they do have caring relationships of some sort, though 18/61 report that they are married or partnered, this suggests that many of the marriages are not within a close relationship now.

25% FtM say this has changed since changeover, that they felt more caring, whilst the MtF 40% reported that this has changed since their changeover.

75% do report that they did have caring relationships of some sort (hugs, closeness etc.) before changeover, though this reduces by 15% after changeover. Against that most report that they felt more able to express their emotional closeness to others.

That suggests that both groups are able to feel more caring, perhaps integrated, since their change of gender role, but because of the circumstances this is not within a one to one partnership.

Over the years we have counselled very many transexed and transgendered people. What is striking is how many have almost no really close relationships. One would imagine loneliness was a real problem for some of the respondents.

In the survey we asked them to
List in order their six most important emotional relationships.
The responses indicated clear trends:
There were 51 replies: 36 from MtF -TS, 8 - TG, 2 - TV & 7 - FtM TS.

However, 34/51 had a partner/wife and these, including 2 ex-wife were higher in importance than other relationships.

For 18/48 the mother (including 2 deceased mothers) is/was the most important, whilst lower in the listing is the father, with 10/48 in the first 6.

Sisters score slightly higher than brothers (8:6), those with no children often include wider family, and these scored 24/51, in this survey.

Children are important but not so important as partner or mother. There were 18/49 who listed sons and 13 who listed daughters, but at a closer proximity to sons.

Transexed people are often accused of irresponsibility because they have been, or are, married and have had children, who may be seen as casualties by the TS and by society as a whole. There is a lot of guilt around about this, as seen in interviews and counselling.

Friends are consistently important, especially female friends. Overall, the TS/TV/TG has more female than male relationships, friendships and degrees of closeness and importance in their selection; 69 female relatives and friends are closest, against 36 male. After partner/wife, friends score higher than family in general, with 32 listed, including 3 who list other TG/TS people as close to them, which emphasises the importance of networking.

There were some unusual inclusions. "My farm, Pets, God, Christians, Dance partner, Lesbian network".

There were some sad remarks: 3 "All dead", 4 "Dead mother". Loss can be an issue when you are over 50.

In terms of the *six most important emotional relationships*, there were some interesting results:

9 Electrologist, 3 G.P., 3 Psychologist, 2 Counsellor, 1 Hairdresser, 1 Speech therapist, 1 Psychiatrist.

It would seem the Electrologist, with whom the MtF generally spends many hours, is in a close emotional place for many of her clients, and yes, even the much-misunderstood psychiatrist is included.

We asked

If they felt there were any particular physical problems in forming relationships? 7 say "None", one adds "I've got a great dog too!" "None save that as post-op I'm a 50 year old woman"

Here we group them:

(Passing): 2 say "Facial hair", 3 say "Telephone voice", "My voice", "Large hands, heavy build" "Height - I'm 6 foot 3 inches tall".

(Surgery) 2 "Not yet post-op", "I lack a phallus", "Lack of penis" "Phalloplasty problems, incontinence, fear", "I need colovaginoplasty plus clitoroplasty"

(Non G.D. Specific problems): "Nobody wants a relationship with anyone this old" "Renal failure", "Eyesight", "Age", "Obsessional compulsive washing disorder" "Work related hearing defect",

Sex - Any Sexual Difficulties?

Half the MtF's say they do not have difficulty with sexual relationships, but a quarter post-op MtF's say they are not interested in sex at all.

The 8 MtF not opting for surgery was asked if they had sexual difficulties.

One said, "I have been impotent all my life", another "I have little need for orgasm"

Half this group said this was not a problem.

In the pre-op MtF group one said "I am neither one sex or the other", another said "I lack the appropriate sex organs".

One in eight were not clear yet about this, it was "on hold". Asked if those who had no orgasm felt they were sexually frustrated 2 pre-op FtM replied "Yes", 1 post-op FtM replied "No", whilst 4 could attain orgasm.

1 post-op MtF was frustrated by no orgasm, 10 pre-op MtF were frustrated.

It is a difficult time.

None of the no-surgery MtF group said they were sexually frustrated. 50% of the FtM's say that they do not have satisfactory sexual relationships. Asked if the lack of orgasm was accompanied by emotional frustration none of the FtM's felt this, but 10% of the MtF's did so, including 1 post-op. This seems to indicate that this survey group takes a generally pragmatic approach.

Over half those in the survey seem to feel that sex is relatively unimportant.

Experience of Sex?
In the context of sexual experience, the post-op group were asked if they had experienced:
Any physical ill effects of their surgery?
None reported persistent labial or vaginal pain post-op.

However 3/14 MtF and 1/6 FtM had some soreness post-op, which resolved in most cases. 1/6 FtM had infections post-op, as did 2/14 MtF. Most recognised the need for caution in the immediate postoperative period and reported some discomfort and anxiety during this time.

The pre-op FtM's all say that the sexual side of their relationships are good, but only one says he has a good sex-life, whilst the post-ops say it is unsatisfactory. However half said the emotional and physical side of their relationship is good or satisfactory.

Among the post-op women only the lesbian partner says sex is good, however half say their sex-life is satisfactory.

Interestingly half avoided the question.

The TV's said sex was good; whilst all but one of the pre-op MtF's said it is non-existent. They are celibate, asexual or simply caring. However half said that the emotional side is good, but 1/3 say that it is emotionally painful or unsatisfactory.

The same sort of figures is true for physical satisfaction without orgasm.

There is considerable evidence of loneliness and avoidance of sex generally, particularly among the pre-op MtF group.

Were able to achieve orgasm, including by masturbation?
Most of the FtM's could, only half the pre-op MtF's could, and half the post-op FtM could.

One wonders if clitoroplasty will make a difference in this respect?

It could be that the pre-op group has more problems with body image and emotional blocks and swings. They are also suffering the effects of Anti-androgens and Oestrogens in high doses.

It would seem the pre-op group suffers most anguish and isolation emotionally and physically, with high levels of distress and confusion. This suggests that the period spent pre-op should not extend beyond the year proposed in the Standards of Care if at all possible.

We asked an optional question about *how these people achieved orgasm.*

The FtM were less shy than the MtF's. Half answered, whilst 9/33 of the pre-ops and half the post-op MtF answered.

The FtM's answered:

1 vaginal penetration with fingers, 2 x clitoral stimulation, 1 anal penetration, 1 pornography, 1 fetish.

Among the pre-op MtF's were answers

'Straight' sex = penile penetration 5, Being fellated 3, Pornography 2. Fetish 1, Giving cunnilingus 1,

Among the post-op MtF's the results were:

Having penile penetration 3. Having vagina penetrated with fingers 3, Having vagina penetrated with sex toys 3. Clitoral stimulation 3, Labial stimulation 2, Having cunnilingus 2, pornography 1.

This suggests that the post-op MtF and FtM are the two groups still interested in sex, at least more so than the pre-op MtF's.

Did They Have Satisfactory Sexual Relationships?

50% of the FtM's say that they do not have satisfactory sexual relationships. Asked if the lack of orgasm was accompanied by emotional frustration none of the FtM's felt this, but 10% of the MtF's did so, including 1 post-op.

This seems to indicate that this survey group takes a generally pragmatic approach.

In the context of sexual experience, the post-op group was asked if they had experienced any physical ill effects or pain after their surgery. None reported persistent labial or vaginal pain post-op. One in four suffered post-op soreness and infection. Most recognised the need for caution in the immediate postoperative period and reported some discomfort and anxiety during this time.

There is considerable evidence of loneliness and avoidance of sex generally, particularly among the pre-op MtF group.

Partners?

Over half the gender dysphoric people interviewed had a partner prior to acknowledging their gender dysphoria. The FtM's tend to have female partners, whilst the MtF's also have female partners, although 1/5 of the MtF have never had a partner.

174

Almost all MtF met their original and present partners in a 'heterosexual' context, whilst the FtM's are split between 'lesbian' and heterosexual context.

All partners save one of a pre-op MtF have been told of their partners gender dysphoria, so it seems most partners are told (or find out) about this difficulty.

Most FtM's do not marry, whilst most MtF's do some time prior to changeover. Only one FtM had married, but is divorced, whilst 80% of the MtF had been or still were married. Of these 7 of the TV/TG people had married more than once, two thrice, whilst 3 of the post-op MtF women had married twice, one remaining with her second wife.

It would suggest from the originally classified 'male' group that one third of those who married did so more than once.

Most of post-op MtF are divorced, though some stay with their spouse. The majority of long term TV or TG people seems to be divorced or living alone. Just over half our sample that assessed themselves as pre-op TS was still living with their spouse.

Only 25% of the post-op MtF group stated that they were still living with their spouse.

Of the FtM all, save the one who once was married, have always had female partners, one is still with his original 'lesbian' partner.

Among the MtF's 16% were widowed. This loss has freed them to live out the rest of their lives as women. Half of the MtF group typically had at some time married, whilst 20% had divorced "Because of their gender dysphoria". It was interesting that 40% of the MtF group were married or partnered, whilst only 20% of the FtM's were.

Sexual Satisfaction?

Less than half who had relationships said that it was good or satisfactory. Others said things like, "We are just friends", "I have non-existent satisfaction", "Good at first, then nothing", "Didn't work out for us", "Unbearable",

"I was disgusted with the sexual side". We would suggest that as revulsion with the male body intensifies the sexual side of things becomes increasingly painful and unrealistic for some couples who started out in a heterosexual relationship together.

The changing body and temperament in response to hormones, then surgery, of a partner is a challenge to both individuals in physical and libidinal terms. Many seem to put sex on hold, or leave it in the realms of daydreams.

Two-thirds of those who talked about their marriages said that they once had sexually satisfying relationships, although there were some who said, "It was emotionally painful to always have to be the man". Half the transgenderists were still with their wife, whilst a quarter of the post-op MtF's were still living with their original partner.

The FtM group has close, but among our survey group, not sexually satisfactory relationship with their partner. Very few have children from their lives before changeover.

Of the 14 post-op MtF women only 1 of this group has a sexual relationship with her original partner. The pre-op group rarely does have a sexual relationship with their original partner; 1/3 is either asexual or celibate. This could be the effect of hormones and reduced libido in some, whilst in others there are the effects of ageing and more particularly, of any hostility felt by a woman who is a partner of a person who is becoming a woman, and therefore ceasing to be a man. While a wife may stay with her husband in these circumstances it is rare that she can easily switch to "being a lesbian".

In fact 70% of the MtF group originally had a sexual relationship with their original wife or partner, and the figures are no different between the post-op group and the others. This suggests that whatever the gender, there is some sex drive, some effort at being 'normal', a wish exists to have a loving relationship and children, and somehow for the 'gender thing' to go away.

Among the post-op MtF group, the 33% who have partners, they are supportive. Pre-op, half the partners are seen as supportive, but the remaining group is not, or is hostile. This suggests that partners are supportive, save when challenged by the pre-op situation.

Half the FtM's would like a partner, and 3/4 of the MtF group still think in terms of having a partner. Overall, one in 3 of the FtM groups describe themselves as asexual or celibate.

Sexual Preference?

Each of the 8 FtM's saw himself as heterosexual, and their relationships were with women, though one of the partners of a FtM saw herself as a lesbian. Most are still seeking a female partner.

It can be a problem for a lesbian if she finds that her 'lesbian' partner is becoming a man, and this can be just as disruptive as it is for a heterosexual woman whose man is becoming a woman.

Most of the partners of the MtF TV's and the pre-op TS's see themselves as heterosexual, though 10% were celibate or asexual, one describes himself as androgynous bisexual.

Among the post-op MtF's three partners see themselves as heterosexual, although they are women living with women now, whilst one is a lesbian and seems to have a good sexual relationship with her partner. However 3/4 of this group have no partner.

Half the MtF pre-op group who have a partner are with women and see themselves as heterosexual, only 2 are with a male partner, one of whom is a TV.

Half the post-op MtF women have no partner, and those who have are 3 to 1 with a female, only one being in a physical relationship with her partner.

One wonders how much of this is by choice and how much a pragmatic response to being 'different' as a TS, the effect of hormones or of the surgery? Certainly about 10% seem confused and uncertain, and some seem to feel that they 'should' be heterosexual and fancy men although they never have in the past. Some 10% keep their options open or describe themselves as bisexual.

Change of Sexual Preference Since Changeover?

Only 1/7 of the FtM's said there had been, whilst 25% of MtF's said there was such a change.

Our observation is that many TS people experience an experimental phase when they want to try out the new equipment. There is both curiosity and fear, but if you talk about dreams many would wish to be "just normal woman with normal feelings and bodies". Another said, "I've always longed to feel a man's loving arms round me … but I think now it's too late".

177

There is a sense in which many seem to need to act out heterosexuality in their new sex (we say this in the anatomical sense) as a phase before re-establishing their original or actual sex preference(s).

Sexual orientation does not usually seem to change in response to hormones, but in this over 50's group of post-op MtF people one third of those who are celibate would like to have a male lover, and their preference at least in fantasy or aspiration has changed. However 25% of the these post-ops would like to be or are lesbians.

Children of Gender Dysphoric People in this Sample?

Of the 61 who completed the questionnaire, 36 had had children in the past. Remembering that 70% had been in a marriage or loving sexual relationship, one can say that almost all who married had children.

None of the FtM group here had a child, and one gathers that it is quite rare for a FtM to have had a child, most have relationships with women, and it is more usual for their partner to have a child by donor, a previous relationship, by A.I.D. or adoption. However this is far from easy.

As yet we know of very few cases of FtM's that were mothers. Whereas post-op MtF's find it hard to officially be allowed to adopt in England. Some do have a child or children from their lives before changeover. All in this survey have children from before their changeover.

In this 50-plus-group most seem to have waited, or been obliged to wait until their children are grown up, or are old enough to accommodate to this change, before their father becomes a woman.

Those of the 27 TS's, who did not have children, were either not ever involved in a relationship where this might be possible, or in a few cases wished they might have been the mother, rather than the more pragmatic and confusing situation of being the father.

Those who married hoped things might turn out well in the end.

However one person had 5 children, two had 4, eleven had 3, thirty-four had 2, and five had one child, making 119 in all. That is 63 girls and 56 boys.

What Were the Children's Ages and Level of Acceptance of their TransParent - in the view of that parent?

Bad or poor levels of acceptance seem to run in families, though one or two are split between siblings. Six groups of children don't know officially or have not been told.

These seem divided between those under 18 years old and those in their middle thirties who were not told and are distant now. In two families half the children do not officially know.

The whole thing of family secrets seems to be a minefield. When, what and how to tell the children and grandchildren seems to be a real problem.

Telling and Levels of Acceptance?

In the Group and telephone interviews 'telling' those close to a subject was very frightening. You can not un-tell. What do you say? How do you say it to a spouse who you still love - passing the burden of this truth to another? How would it affect children? At what age is best to tell them (least damaging)? Who have you told of your Gender Dysphoria?

(49/61 replied)

10% have told nobody, 2% told everybody. 80% told close friends, 50% told acquaintances.

It seems to be less fraught telling people outside the immediate family.

Telling a partner, then the children seems to be very difficult for fear of profound emotional consequences.

Not telling is more dangerous still, if they find out or are told by someone else, it seems harder for them to come to terms with the adjustments they may need to make. One partner, some young children, and some adult children who have left home have not been told.

Level of Acceptance of Relatives:					
	Good	Fair	Poor	Bad	Deceased
Mother	14/47	2/47	2/47	4/47	25/47
Father	7/47	2/47	2/47	1/47	35/47
Siblings	18/39	9/39	2/39	4/39	4/39
Rest of Family	22/41	12/41	1/41	4/41	2/41

Relationship Difficulties that were Listed:
"Don't want to lose happy marriage"
"I relate to females as a female",
"Mother pretends I'm dead"
"Lost family, hostile kids"
"Confidence needed"
"Difficult to get close to others"
"Shy, save on 1 to 1 basis".

We asked if they felt there were any particular physical problems they had in forming relationships. 7 say "None", one adds "I've got a great dog too!" "None save that as post-op I'm a 50 year old woman"

We asked respondents to rank a number of situations in order of importance:
(1 to 8)
1. For the majority, recognising that they had a gender identity problem was the most important.
2. A close second was the start of hormones.
3. Third in importance was going out dressed in public for the first time, as they felt they should be.
4. Fourth was the first time they dressed as a member of the preferred (actual) gender.
5. Fifth in rank was choosing a name.
6. The first time they worked in role was next.
7. Surgery,
8. Followed by their first relationship post-op.

What seems to be interesting is that hormones come so high in this list, as though if they recognise the dysphoria, they need to start on hormones, before they have chosen a name, know if they will fit into society (pass) or dress as a member of their believed gender. The reaction is not generally cognitive or practical, but emotional.

It also seems to be saying "Let's get the body right, before we worry if it will work out well". The list for the recently post-ops, and immediately pre-ops puts more emphasis on surgery and subsequent relationships.

In a sense this list maps out the life course of the transexed person as a rite of passage, with steps to be taken in a certain order.

Reactions seem to be very immediate, rather than a stroll along a prescribed path, or a stratagem for success as in an exam.

STRESSES, LOSSES and GAINS: (We have grouped the responses) ***LOSSES*** experienced are listed here:

(Relationships)
Nothing significant. 17 None.
I can't think what, None - but the death of my wife is my sorrow
Impending split. Telling and causing mental anguish to wife.
Wonderful marriage. Marriage over. Weaker marriage.
Marriage.

Close family. 2 Family life. Being a father to my children.
Contact with my daughter. My daughter. 2 daughters.
Rejection by my son when told of it. Older sister
Lost children.

Mother's hostility. Mother. Friends contact,
Causing stress to family. . No cuddles
Distress at pain caused to loved ones. House, Holidays
Home.

Temporary rejection from some people. Rejection by some friends.
Some old friends. Some so-called friends. Some female friends. Friends.
2 Financial. 2 Status.
Forced early retirement.

Difficult to put in writing. Confusion. Negativity. Isolation.
Contacts.
Lack of encouragement. Lack of energy.
Ageing
(Passing): 2 say "Facial hair" 3 say "Telephone voice", "My voice", "Large hands, heavy build"
(Surgery) "Not yet post-op", "I lack a phallus" "Lack of penis" "Phalloplasty problems, incontinence, fear"
(Non G.D. Specific problems): "Obsessional compulsive washing disorder" "Work related hearing defect" "Renal failure" "Eyesight", "Age",

181

The Worst Problems experienced are listed here in broad groups. ("None" was expressed by 4) - each phrase is from a separate respondent.

"Ridicule of teenagers and lower classes. Confrontation by Afro-Caribbeans.

Harassment from local yobs, Public opprobrium, Opposition of people, Closed minds

Being read. Children's questions at first. Being known locally 2 x Read by children.

Religious fanatics, I was sent to Coventry. Prejudice from some men. Intolerance.

Not being accepted at work. Not accepted in local group Reputation suffered-disclosure.

Disclosure. Coming to terms with having to leave my loved one."

3 x deciding and telling and helping wife to come to terms.

Coming to terms. Trying to keep partner, 2 Persuading daughter

Having to work as a man for the sake of the family

Not having the courage to tell my friends, Resisting urge to be full-time, Not finding the relationship I want, Not changing because of my family,"

"Being rejected by my family, Rejection by mother, Messy divorce, Lost brother, Isolation. My true path to femininity is obstructed, Being ripped off by Transformation"

"Slowness of physical changes, Slowness of electrolysis, Cystitis at first, now all right

Nervous breakdowns at ages 45 & 58. Short of off-the-peg clothes my size"

2 Money. Worse pay. Lack of finance. Loss of job

Being denied employment postop on basis of being seen as mad.

National Insurance insists original sex is correct

Refusal of Australian passport since I'm pre-op

Suffocating bureaucracy delaying changeover

Legal problems. Social services problems

Psychiatrists - they should be castrated

Access to health facilities,

Total lack of medical help
No penis, sexual loss,
2 x Voice too deep,
Toilets difficult,
Height, Beard"

Gains experienced are listed here:
"2 x Happier & 2 x Happiness. Exhilarated at times. Relaxed. 2 x Being myself.

Self-identity. Mental wellbeing. 2 x Confident. 2 x Relief, 2 x Real. Inner peace. Satisfaction. 2 x Contentment. Content with self. 4 x More relaxed. Honesty,

I have acknowledged the way I feel. Emotional openness. Emotional release.

Improved assertiveness, Secure sense of self. Knowing what I am. I have found myself.

I have become myself. Relief I am what I always was - a woman. Happy being female.

Now I know I wasn't just imagining it as a child. I look out at the world, not in at myself.

I have balance with my family. I have an accepting partner.

I am much happier with life as a woman. Living as I was meant to live. Feels right.

Right gender, I am normal after so many years.

Shedding the veneer. 5 x nicer person.

Much happier person.

Better person - not bad tempered.

More friends. Wider life.

Closer relationships,

Making many Varied friends.

Lots of friends,

Better quality of life.

Less repressed-gosh!   5 x Peace of mind.

Inner scream silenced.   Freedom!

CONCLUSION

It seems that the passing years have been a mixture of struggle and hardship, of triumph and personal fulfilment for the TS's in our study. Paradoxically, it was in some ways easier to be young in the early decades of the century. People were not under pressure to make public their private hopes and ambitions. Whereas today, self-knowledge carries the obligation to act, to be true to oneself, in those days such personal secrets carried no obligation to come out or go public.

On the other hand, there was no pride in one's status, indeed there was great shame. Pride and an obligation to act came in the decades of liberation, the 1960's and 1970's, when dispossessed groups acquired a sense of collective pride and self-respect.

It took until that Conference year, 6th July 1996, for the first TS presence to be visible at the National Gay Pride Rally in London. Transgender Pride was included as a stated aim of the march.

Not surprisingly, there is now a sense of regret among older TS's. "I wish I had known at 20 what I know now", is a common statement in later life. For the TS, though, the availability of information, together with improved surgical results, could have made an enormous difference to the pace of change. The sense of relief at having finally arrived at the chosen destination after years of struggle was powerful. "I wouldn't like to live my life over again!"

The relief might be short-lived, for those still in the queue for surgery. There is a sense in this group of being once more misunderstood and denied opportunities. This time, advanced age is the basis for discrimination. The over 60's have problems getting help through the NHS. Present trends are ageist. Even the G.I.C. at Charing Cross appears to use age as a basis for denying treatment.

184

70. A Qualitative and Quantitative Survey of 102 Transpeople 1990/2

I now include a Survey completed in 1992 and presented to the GENDYS Conference that year:

An Assessment of Treatments and Follow Up on a group of 102 Transexed People. Researcher Alice Purnell RGN, B.Sc.

(At that time attending the University of Brighton and was a Nursing Manager, Psychologist, and the GENDYS Conference Organiser).

Also the Chairperson Beaumont Trust, and the Gender Trust (which she founded),

Editor of GEMSNews at the time. Overseas Representative of the Beaumont Society

In 1987 as Medical Researcher on behalf of S.H.A.F.T., (The SELF HELP ASSOCIATION FOR TRANSSEXUALS founded by Judy Cousins in 1980).

In the Nineties we were concerned about the appalling lack of research into any sort of longitudinal studies or follow-up work (We still are!).

Almost no research involved a reasonably large sample, so their validity from a scientific perspective was questionable. Looking through the *Index Medicus* and all the Psychiatric and Psychology Journals, there was almost no information for professionals in this field of work. Few abstracts or studies had been published regarding the care, medication, and assessment, monitoring of pre- and post-operative transexed people. There was what seemed to be a great gap left by the much under-resourced N.H.S. in the Gender Identity Clinics.

Concern was also felt regarding the apparent lack of attention which appeared to exist in the U.K. to proper Standards of Care*: which, we felt, should apply in the U.K., although there were American Standards which were loosely followed here.

(*As proposed and agreed by the Harry Benjamin Gender Dysphoria Association of international experts involved in the care and treatment of Transsexuals - and to be reviewed and applied in the UK.).

This apparent lack, in particular in respect of the post-operative group, combined with an absence of research by the drug companies gave rise to curiosity, if not concern about long-term-effects, effectiveness and side-effects of medications, of surgery, to the lives of transexed patients. This concern was reinforced by the lack of published work in the UK on a scientific or statistical basis to demonstrate that things were being done in the best possible way for these people.

Numbers of diagnosed and self-diagnosed patients who presented themselves to the G.I.C.'s had increased dramatically in the seventies, and yet diminishing resources were and are available to treat them. Psychiatrists, Physicians and GP's who prescribe hormones to TS's are rather out on a limb as prescribers, in that the drug companies deny that these substances are being used for this population, and have not themselves published any guidelines in the Formulary or MIMS.

Post-operative TS's are a difficult group to monitor since they tend to change address during or early after treatment and it is reasonable that they should wish to merge with the general population as 'well people', not as "transsexuals" undergoing ongoing treatment.

Quite understandably they try to avoid identification or 'ghettoisation' by not remaining connected with the G.I.C.'s or self help groups.

However the problems do not cease with surgery, and the medications continue for many years. Relatively high doses of Oestrogens and Progestogens in the cases of male to female TS's, and of Androgens in the case of FtM TS's, are maintained pre- and post-operatively.

Effects on the liver, cardiovascular system, potential Osteoporosis, Atheroma, Hypertension, Thrombo-embolic disease, mood swings or other effects had not to date been properly reported. **(*Nor are they now in 2004)** It would seem therefore important that assessment in respect of medications etc. be continued.

Some work has been done in respect of adeno-carcinomas and other damage to the liver caused by certain androgenic preparations, which have now been discontinued. It is the long-term effects of the 'safe' preparations in use in treating large populations of trans people, which has not been properly investigated or reported.

This study is not able yet to come to clear conclusions, but is rather to spur the professions to address these matters. This study also intended to gauge the self-assessment of this population of transexed persons. We looked at alcohol and tobacco abuse, and space was left for as many comments on all matters which the respondents wished to insert, these are also included in the survey.

In this statistical and qualitative study various other matters were brought to light, such as sexuality, sexual preference, the reaction apparent from others to the trans person.

The general assumption that transsexualism is about sex, not gender, is in all probability caused by the term "Trans Sexual", which rather implies this incorrect thinking.

The Survey produced results, which I feel clarify this matter. We sought to find the patient's view of how the professions helped them with their problems, in terms of psychiatry, psychology, social work, counselling, monitoring, and all the backups, which were, or were not available.

We also sought to find any familial trait towards gender dysphoria. This was an ambitious project, and of course can not supply definitive answers yet, but it is hoped that the professions themselves and Charities such as the Beaumont Trust and GIRES will maintain this work.

In the survey 250 questionnaires were sent to all of the then members of S.H.A.F.T. and some GEMS members. There were 102 completed questionnaires, representing a 40.8% response. No double blind or control could be taken, but statistics exist elsewhere in this respect, in questions which might be put to the general public. It is hoped that a similar questionnaire might be produced in the future to compare results, utilising the membership of support groups.

All members of S.H.A.F.T. were over 21, the GEMS membership was over 18, so no assessment of children presenting with Gender Dysphoric problems was possible. The problems in 1998 - 1992 were if anything worse in terms of resources.

In a future questionnaire investigations might include HIV incidence and other questions we did not cover here.

In the case of this sample, some help was given by the ex S.H.A.F.T. Membership Secretary Frances Dare, during 1988, for which we were grateful. We are also most grateful to the 102 people who provided the completed questionnaires.

Unfortunately at the time the questionnaire was produced the researcher had no computer, and the questions were designed without planning how to process them using a computer; so this meant a great deal of extra work with the data base and spreadsheet.

I then had an IBM XT, so with improved computers and software it should be easier for future researchers.

In this case there were 65 questions, which with sub-questions made 194 questions, this gave approximately 20,000 items of information to process, together with all written remarks by the respondents; and consequently there were large numbers of results and findings to derive and report. Some questions were not answered by all the respondents, whilst others did not apply.

187

The Results were as follows:

GENDER DIRECTION.

Number of respondents:

	Male to Female	Female to Male	TOTAL
	93	9	102

In the following groups:

	MtF	%	FtM	%
Pre-operative	60	64.5	4	44.5
Post-operative	18	19.4	5	55.5
Undecided	7	7.5	NIL	
Not having the operation	8	8.6	NIL	

AGE in YEARS? (IF POST OP HOW LONG IN YEARS?

	MtF	Av. Range	FtM	Av. Range	
Pre-op	42.5	21 - 66	28	23 - 32	(All were over 21)
Post-op	42.5	33 - 68	43	31 - 67	
Undecided	40.5	26 - 61	NIL		
No-op	57	31 -74	NIL		

There were 96 replies to age,
6 MtF gave no reply.

AGES % OF TOTALS

	MtF	% of M	FtM	% of F	%	Total
in 20's	9	10.3	2	22.2	11	11.5
in 30's	29	33.3	5	55.5	34	35
in 40's	21	24.2	1	11.1	22	23
in 50's	16	18.5	-	-	16	16.5
over 60	12	13.8	1	11.1	13	13.5

CONCLUSION: Most respondents were in their 30's, and from both groups. The MtF's were more sensitive about their age.

IF PRE-OP, WHICH OP'S DO YOU INTEND TO HAVE?

There were 60 MtF replies and 4 FtM replies.
All 60 MtF's said they wanted gender reassignment (vaginoplasty)
10 x wanted breast implants. 7.x Rhinoplasty (nose jobs),
5..x Facial surgery, 3.x Adam's apple correction, 1.x Lip surgery,
1.x Shoulders and rib reduction, 1.x Hands and feet reduction!
The 4 pre-op FtM's all wanted gender reassignment, which they defined as mastectomy and hysterectomy. None mentioned phalloplasty here.

188

CONCLUSION: The difficulties of creating a reasonable phallus surgically have deterred many FtM's from this option. The build of the MtF often results in difficulty in passing, even with plastic surgery.

HEIGHT IN INCHES. (60"= 5 FEET TALL!)

		Average	Range.
FtM	Pre op	65"	64" to 68".
	Post op	64"	62" to 65".

CONCLUSION: FtM's tend to be short as compared to a range of men.

	Average	Range
M to F Pre op	67"	62" to 74"
Post op	68.5"	62" to 74"
Undecided	68.5"	66" to 71"
No surgery	68.5"	63" to 72"

CONCLUSION: Height is not a consideration for the TS herself or himself, although it can create a difficulty.

4 MtF post op failed to give height - this may be a sensitive issue for them

WEIGHT IN POUNDS.

		Average	Range
FtM	Pre op	144 lb.	124 lb. - 161 lb.
	Post op	125 lb.	112 lb. - 135 lb.
MtF	Pre op	148 lb.	119 lb. - 190 lb.
	Post op	158 lb.	117 lb. - 203 lb.
	Undecided	154 lb.	122 lb. - 170 lb.
	No surgery	152 lb.	133 lb. - 182 lb.

CONCLUSION: Increase in weight as in the general population, seems to be a factor of height, age, and body build and in the MtF TS how long on Oestrogens in high doses.

IN YOUR OPINION ARE YOU:
TALL/AVERAGE/SHORT?

FtM	Pre-op		2 average.	2 short.
	Post op			5 short.
MtF	pre op	26 tall.	29 average.	5 short.
	Post op	10 tall.	5 average.	1 short.
	Undecided	3 tall.	4 average.	1 short.
	No surgery	3 tall.	4 average.	1 short.

IN YOUR OPINION ARE YOU:
OBESE/MEDIUM/SLENDER /THIN?

FtM	pre-op		3 medium.	1 slender.
	Post-op		4 medium.	1 slender.
MtF	pre-op	2 obese.	33 medium	21 slender.
	Post op	2 obese.	8 medium.	5 slender.
	Undecided	2 obese.	3 medium.	2 slender.
	No surgery	2 obese	3 medium.	3 slender.

CONCLUSION: There is a tendency to self perception in MtF TS's as being obese, in actuality this is the case. Self-perceptions of body frame are reasonably realistic.

HAVE YOU EVER SMOKED?

Of those 55 who answered yes:
MtF total   51 of 93
          (37 pre-op, 3 no-op, 8 post-op 3 undecided)
FtM total   4 of 9 (2 pre-op and 2 post-op)
5 out of 18 post-ops MtF gave up before surgery. 2 out of 5 Post-op FtM's still are smokers after surgery.
CONCLUSION: Tendency to smoke tobacco is diminishing in line with national trends. It is known tobacco smoking is contra-indicated especially prior to surgery.

DO YOU SMOKE NOW?

Of the 102 who replied to the questionnaire 26 said they still smoke. 12 Failed to answer the question whether they smoked.

IF SO, HOW MANY A DAY?

Pre-op MtF, 17 yes:	FtM, 2 yes:	Post-op MtF, 3 yes:	FtM, 2 yes:
10 - 20 a day 6	10 - 20 a day 2	10 - 20 a day 2	10 - 20 a day 2
20 - 30 a day 5		20 - 30 a day 1	
30 - 40 a day 4			
40 - 50 a day 1			
60 a day 1			

MtF undecided 3 smoked, 2 gave up, remaining smoker had 20 a day.
MtF no surgery 1 smoked 10 a day.
Of the whole sample of 102, 26 (25%) still smoke, 55-26=29 gave up.

IF YOU GAVE UP SMOKING, HOW LONG AGO IN YEARS?

2 gave up under 2 years earlier.   3 gave up between 2 & 3 years earlier.
4 gave up between 4 & 5 years earlier. 2 gave up between 6 & 10 years earlier.
18 more than 10 yrs earlier.

CONCLUSION: Although TS's tend to suffer depression and stress the majority have either stopped smoking or never smoked. This may reflect in this way because the greater portion of respondents here are MtF, one has the impression that a larger percentage of FtM TS's smoke, than MtF's, but there is not a large enough sample here to bear this out.

WOULD YOU DESCRIBE YOURSELF AS ALCOHOLIC?
HAVE YOU EVER USED ALCOHOL TO EXCESS?

8% of the sample described themselves as alcoholic, while 47% of all respondents say that they have used alcohol to excess.

There were 54 answers to the first question and 53 to the second.

To the first question 4 described themselves as alcoholics = 8% of sample.

Of the 53 that replied to the second question, 25 (=47%) say that they had used alcohol
to excess, 27 (=51%) had not.

COMMENT: Alcohol is an escape also a depressant, it can be a problem for gender dysphoric people.

ARE YOU ON ANY NON FEMALE OR MALE HORMONE MEDICATIONS?
and LIST OTHER MEDICATIONS.

A total of 25 respondents take additional medications.

NB (TDS = 3x a day, bd = twice, nocte = at night, prn = when required)

FtM's (2 take other medications)

FtM post-op   1.x Tenormin 100 mg (Antihypertensive) & Thyroxin 150 mcg
FtM pre-op: 1 x Colofac 135-mg prn. & Prothiaden 75 mg nocte.

MtF's (23 take other medications)

MtF post-op. (5 Take other medications)

a. Bromocriptine 2.5 mg (to stop lactation) Palfium prn for electrolysis pain
b. Betadine vaginal gel, daily, prn.
c. Moduretic 1 (mornings).
d. Inderal (Antihypertensive) 160 mg.
e. Warfarin (anticoagulant) 3 mg.

MtF no-surgery (2 take non hormone medications)

a. Nifidipine 10 mg.
b. Nifidipine 20 mg. Allopurinol 300 mg.

MtF pre-op (13 take other medications)

a. Piriton 4 mg tds, (plus Copraximol - max 8 a day to stop electrolysis pain)
b. Temazepam 20 mg 1 nocte
c. Vit E
d. Multivit (3 take this)
e. Librium 10 mg, Prothiaden 75 mg, Dihydrocodeine for pain.
f. Minoxidil cream 1% (tries to promote scalp hair regrowth)
g. Dipyridamole 100mg, Aspirin 75 mg 1 a day.
h. Various vitamin & mineral supplements
i. Nardil 45 mg
j. Burinex 1 mg bd.
k. Lorazepam 0.5 mg, Dalmene 15 mg.

MtF undecided (3 take other medications)

a. Prothiaden 25 mg
b. Minoxidil 2% (applied to scalp for hair restoration)
c. Imipramine 10 mg, Slow-Trasicor 160 mg, Nifidipine 20 mg

SUMMARY:

6 MtF 's are on anti hypertensives and coronary vasodilators
(3 Nifidipine, 1 Dipyridamole, 1 Inderal, 1 Slow-Trasicor).
3 MtF's are on antidepressant (Imipramine, Prothiaden, Nardic)
1 MtF is on an Anxiolytic (Lorazepam)
2 MtF's are on sedatives (Librium, Temazepam)

CONCLUSION: 6% of the MtF's are being treated for hypertension. This is not a particularly strange result for a sample of similar age from the UK. We can not say whether those with hypertension reflect a reaction to the problems of gender dysphoria, or a response to long term use of Oestrogens, or to the recognised mechanisms exhibited in the general populace - it is impossible to say with so small a sample.

N.B. A point to bear in mind is that only a small percentage are having their blood pressure monitored by either the G.I.C. or the G.P.

ARE YOU ON ANY HORMONES?
ORAL OR INTRAMUSCULAR PREPARATIONS - DOSE RATE?

FtM pre-op 4/4 replied yes.
2 given i/m Testosterone once a month.
1 took Restandol 200 mg a day
 took Restandol 120 mg a day.

FtM post-op 3/5 replied yes
1 took Testosterone 25 mg bd, 1 given Sustanon 250 intramuscular each 4 weeks.
1 given Sustanon 100 intramuscular each 2 weeks.1 took no hormones, 1 no reply.

MtF pre-op. 53 replied yes
46 took Premarin, 40/46 took 2.5 mg t.d.s. = 7.5 mg a day. Other daily dose rates varied below this.
13 took Androcur (Cyproterone Acetate) 50 mg a day. 2 took Diane 2 mg a day (2mg Cyproterone Acetate + 0.05 mg Ethinyloestradiol)
1 took Ethinyloestradiol 10 mcg, 1 took Stilboestrol 10 mg.

CONCLUSION: The most usual regime was 7.5 mg a day Premarin in conjunction with Androcur 50 mg.

MtF no surgery (4, took the following):
1 took Ethinyloestradiol 5 mcg a day, 1 took Premarin 7.5 mg a day
1 took Premarin 1.25 mg + Androcur 50mg, 1 took Premarin 0.625 mg a day

MtF undecided (4, took the following):
1 took Premarin 7.5 mg + Androcur 100 mg, 1 took Premarin 6.25 mg
1 took Diane 2 a day. 1 took Premarin 2.5 mg

MtF post-op 14 (they took the following):*
2 took Premarin 7.5 mg, 1 took Premarin 5 mg, 4 took Premarin 2.5 mg
1 took Premarin 5mg ~+ Androcur 50mg bd + Bromocriptine 2.5mg
2 took Premarin 2.5 mg + Provera 5 mg,
1 took Premarin 2.5 mg + Provera 5 mg once a week.
2 took Premarin 1.25 mg, 1 took Androcur 50 mg + Ethinyloestradiol 0.01 mg
1 took Diane 2 mg., 2 took no Hormones, and 2 did not answer

CONCLUSION:

75/93 MtF TS's said they took female hormones = 81% total.

7/9 FtM TS's said they took male hormones = 77.8% total.

It seems strange that over a year post op an Antiandrogen was still being prescribed to a patient.

2 Persons had no reduction of dose rate or strength post op.

It would seem post op medication regimes of Oestrogens were rather ad hoc, but on the positive side some cases seem to be tailor made.

The administration of Progestogen is advisable for breast enhancement, in addition to a reasonably low dosage maintenance dose of conjugated Oestrogens post op for MtF TS's, and of some testosterone for FtM TS's. Progestogen with Oestrogen, for FtM, or androgen may help reduce the possibility of osteoporosis in either case.

SUMMARY OF HORMONES & SURGERY MtF:

Surgery:
Of the MtF post-op's:
7 were a year post-op, 4 were 2 years post-op
2 were 3 years post-op
(1 had several attempts at improving poor result, 1 required labial surgery.)
1 was 4 years post-op - earlier had to have hair growing inside her vagina removed.
1 was 5 years post-op - had no vaginoplasty.
1 was 6 years post-op - had urethral repair, then needed to have a colostomy section attached to the vagina
1 was 7 years post-op
1 was 11 years post-op - Had 4 unsuccessful attempts at improving poor result.

Surgery:
Of the FtM post-op's:
2/5 had phalloplasty, One had 9 ops total.
1 took over 2 years and had mastectomy 3 yrs earlier,
1 in one-stage bilateral mastectomy 8 yrs earlier
1 had mastectomy only, no hysterectomy - 8 years earlier
1 had mastectomy & hysterectomy 8 yrs. earlier
1 had bilateral mastectomy 2 yrs. earlier and hysterectomy 1 year.

Hormones:

The FtM's on 'male' hormones:

The voice breaks, all develop male type hair distribution,
They have a 3/4 chance of a weight increase, of an average of 16 lb.
There is a 1/4 chance of depression, a 2/3 increase in sexual libido,
Moods are less variable, but there is a tendency to feel more aggressive.
There is a 1/4 tendency to balding, a 2/5 of increase in physical strength, 2/3 have facial hair (They often have beards). Acne is a problem when they start androgens.

Of the 18 MtF post-op's:

33% have depression,
46% have a weight increase of an average of 21.5 Lb.
There is a 55% chance of loss of libido, half of the total lose it entirely.
Others report it is different post op. Some change sexual preference.
Half find decreased regrowth of facial hair when on hormones and having electrolysis.
20% are euphoric. 40% found their strength has diminished.
Breasts develop in many in this group.
All generally appeared happier.

Of the 75 MtF - un-operated group:

There is a 12% reports of depression, 10% sleep disturbance.
40% report an average weight increase of 16 lb.
There is a 50% chance of lost libido - which is reversible in many cases - but which often occurred before administration of hormones.
30% have mood changes, many of the remarks on mental habitus were very positive, but rather stereotypical, like "passive", "gentle" etc.
Improved skin texture is reported,
30% have improved head hair, 25% report good breast development.
Many report brittle fingernails - helped by taking cod liver oil tabs.,
1 Stroke reported, hypertension a problem; blood pressure should be monitored.

The effects of gender-specific medicines and hormones are still to be explored.

195

Female to Male:

SINCE YOU STARTED ON HORMONES, DO YOU HAVE ANY TENDENCY TO:

DEPRESSION? 2 total, =22.2%   "Slight", "when I had periods."

SLEEPLESSNESS?   Nil.

WEIGHT INCREASE? 7 total, =77.7%; Average weight up 16 lb. Slight, gained 8 lb., 2x gained 14 lb., gained 28 lb., "at first a lot - now a bit overweight", "yes, earlier on when on methyl testosterone."

WEIGHT LOSS?   Nil.

LOSS OF SEXUAL LIBIDO?   Nil

INCREASE OF SEXUAL LIBIDO? 6 total, =66.6%.
"For first few years", "varies", "yes - good thing", "increase has remained", "dramatic first", "very high - curbed by masturbation".

MOOD CHANGES?
"mood is more stable", "but more aggressive", "Not since hormones", "far less on hormones", "feel aggressive in tense situations", "more aggressive", "yes".

INDIGESTION: 1 yes

DECREASE IN HAIR GROWTH/HEAD? 2 total, =22.2%
"Hair loss", "hair receded".

INCREASE IN BODY HAIR: 9 total = 100%
3x yes, "yes - good", 2x "body hair male - even on chest",
"hair around nipples and on stomach",   2x "slight",

INCREASE FACIAL HAIR: 6 total, =66.6%,
2x yes, "hardly noticeable", "yes - good have beard", and "slight".

WATER RETENTION? "took Moduretic before coming off hormones".

BLOOD PRESSURE INCREASES? 1. "High BP. - Controlled with Tenormin".

LIVER COMPLAINTS?   Nil.

EUPHORIA?   Nil.

LOSS OF PHYSICAL STRENGTH?   Nil.

INCREASE OF PHYSICAL STRENGTH? 4 total, =44.4%
Yes x 3, "increased - I also do weight training".

TENDENCY TO SUICIDE? 1x "when he was depressed".

ANY OTHER EFFECTS? Male baldness pattern, loose bowels after injection, clitoris larger 1" when roused. 2x appalling acne at first.

THERE WERE NO DISADVANTAGES LISTED.

FURTHER ADVANTAGES WERE LISTED AS:
Menstrual cycle stopped, Voice broke for 8/9.

Male to Female:

SINCE YOU STARTED ON HORMONES, DO YOU HAVE ANY TENDENCY TO: (Of the 18 MtF post op group):

DEPRESSION? 6 total, =33.3% "Slight", "several times a week", "possibly", "chronic at times lasting weeks", "pre op twice a week".

SLEEPLESSNESS? 3 total, =16.7% "Quite bad", "sporadic", "difficult at first".

WEIGHT INCREASE: 8 total, =44.4% had gained, Average of stated gained = 21.5 lb. "Slight", "tend to get fat", gained 7 lb., gained 12 lb., "gained 25 lb. after op", "up 25% since surgery", "up 42 lb. after started hormones".

WEIGHT LOSS 1x through slimming.

LOSS OF SEXUAL LIBIDO: 10 total, =55.5%
"Not v. interested in sex", "yes until off hormones", "small loss", "male problems gone", "almost total", "halved", "libido v.slight", "loss of libido after hormones", 2x "yes".

INCREASE OF SEXUAL LIBIDO: 3 total, =16.7% - 2 Yes, 1 "up", "after surgery".

MOOD SWINGS: 7x "weepiness", "variable", 3x "yes", "slightly", "lethargic".

INDIGESTION: 1x slight

INCREASE IN HAIR GROWTH ON HEAD: 4 total, =22.2%
"Possible", "good", "slight", "improved".

DECREASE IN REGROWTH OF FACIAL HAIR AFTER ELECTROLYSIS:
10 total, = 55.5%
4x "Yes", 4x "slight", "steady improvement", "better".

WATER RETENTION: 2 total, =11.1%
"Slight", "small amount".

BLOOD PRESSURE INCREASE: 1x "rocketed post op".

EUPHORIA 4 total, =22.2% 2x "At first", "slight", "mild".

198

LOSS OF STRENGTH: 8 total, =44.4%
2 "Yes", "a little", "once post op", "slightly", "1/3 of before", "like a woman's", "loss of strength".

TENDENCY TO SUICIDE: 3 total, =16.7%
"Yes pre op", "had post op stress", "considered it often before surgery".

OTHER EFFECTS: "breasts developing", "loss of hair on legs", "calmness", "waist 2 inches narrower", and "some lethargy".

Of those Remaining 75 MtF TS's who were on Hormones:
DEPRESSION? 17 total, =12.75%:
3x yes, "mild bouts", "occasional weepiness", "sometimes severe", "had lifelong depression - slightly better after hormones", "slight", 2x "very bad while on Androcur", "terrible for months", 2x "varies", "self destructive", "as a result of non referral", "for a few days a week", "v.bad for 2 yrs".

SLEEPLESSNESS? 12 total, =9%:
2 x y, "y - worry", "as a result of non referral", 2x "at first", "2 nights a week", "slightly, due to domestic situation", "generally better", "sometimes", "y -wake early", "only sleep 5 hrs a night".

WEIGHT INCREASE?   28 total, = 37.3%
3 x "Yes", Initially dieting, Yes - I'm glad to say, moderate,
50% increase in body weight- I have to diet now, 8 x slight, 4x gained 7lb, 2x gained 10lb, 1x gained 28lb, 4 gained 14lb, and 2 gained 12lb
Average weight increase was twelve pounds

WEIGHT LOSS? Only due to dieting

LOSS OF SEXUAL LIBIDO? 41 Total- 54.7%
8x Yes, Is it permanent? 2x I have hardly any, Reduced to Nil, Gradual decrease,
Almost non-existent now - never strong anyway, for female partner,
No erections I'm glad to say, Yes - I had prostate removed years ago,
I take Androcur to kill male sex drive, As a Male yes, 2x Decreasing,
I get sexual feelings once a month, halved, slight, Y - for 6 months - it's great.
5x totally lost, Acceptable, At first - returning now, not as much as expected,

Increasing loss, No sex life in 16 years, Yes to great relief, 2x lost libido before treatment, 2x considerable, Gone since started Androcur

INCREASE OF SEXUAL LIBIDO?
6 Total - Though replies indicated libido is different)

MOOD CHANGES: 24 total, =32%
4x y, "yes difficult to handle", "first 3 years - now OK", 3x "up & down",
2x "considerably more emotional", "sudden weepiness", "mild", "prone to tantrums, very bad for 8 months", 2x "slight", "get depressed", 2x "not as marked as before treatment", "brief moodiness", "very occasionally", "frequent short term", "volatile now on hormones - that's better than depression".

INDIGESTION: 9 total, =12%, 3x y, 2 at first, 2x occasional, 2x temporary nausea.

INCREASE IN HAIR ON THE HEAD; 24 total stated improvements
5x y, "y - using hair tonic", "yes - Minoxidil helps", 2x "hairline improving", 2x "texture improved", "moderate", 2x "slight", 3x "grows faster", 4x "thickening",
2x "decrease in loss", "improved after starting Androcur"

INCREASE IN BODY HAIR; 4 stated change. 2x "not increased but finer", 2x "softer".

DECREASE IN REGROWTH AFTER ELECTROLYSIS: total 19, =25.3%
18x "yes", "improved after started Androcur".

WATER RETENTION: 14 total, =18.7%.
4x "slight", 4x "yes", "on thighs & bum", "feet puffy", "y when on Stilboesterol",
3x "on water tabs".

BLOOD PRESSURE INCREASE ON MEDICATION: 4 total
Please note: most patients do not have BP checked
3x "slight", "up from av. 130/80 To 150/90".

LIVER COMPLAINTS: none noted.

EUPHORIA: 12 total, =16%.

5x "yes", 2x "happiness", "y - constantly", "giggle a lot", "wonderful happiness", "felt wonderful since a week after hormones", "happier living as a woman."

LOSS OF PHYSICAL STRENGTH; 28 total, =37.3%

8x "yes", 6 x "slightly", "a little", 4x "pronounced", "especially in arms (Her's that is)", "reduction in stamina", "y - difficult to continue work", "30% less", 2x "gradually less", "half as strong", "female strength", "not as strong as I was but stronger than most girls".

INCREASE OF PHYSICAL STRENGTH - nil

TENDENCY TO SUICIDE; 9 total, =12% "yes".

"Less than before", "I tend to despair because of the waiting", "sometimes",

2x "when referral is delayed", "tried suicide once", "lessened",

"a sense of despair sometimes".

OTHER EFFECTS: 23 other effects total.

"Pains in legs when started Premarin", 5x "fingernails brittle", "decrease in nail biting", "nipples enlarging and breasts", "breasts increased - painful", "bad depression", "less aggressive - inner peace", "calmer", "bust tender - monthly nausea", "facial hair almost stopped", "blood clotting - on treatment", 2x "softer skin tone", "increased girth of hip bones", "morning sickness (on Stilboesterol)", 2x "decrease in body hair", "unable to drink much alcohol now", "general feminisation of body".

POST OP MtF's LISTED FURTHER DISADVANTAGES:

2x "sickness", "short spells of nausea - not since op", "lethargy", "depression", "depression - grieving for bad old self", "waistline increased", "beware all alcohol", "predisposition to thrombosis since hormones".

POST OP MtF's LISTED FURTHER DISADVANTAGES:

nausea x3, tiredness x4, night cramps, "fat stomach because of pills", nails split x6, "spots on face and thighs", "blood clotting. After 3 months this ended", "stroke (aged 50)", "morning sickness", "depression as a result of difficulties of changeover", "nightmares", "sexual dreams", "tender breasts", "dizziness", "indecisive", "crying".

FURTHER ADVANTAGES WERE LISTED BY POST OP MtF's:

"better body shape" x2, "more normal life style", "better sex life -more erotic", "less constipation when on hormones", "acne & eczema cleared up", "happier" x2, "stopped hair loss", "face - features + skin softer", "bust increase", "facial hair finer", "calmer most of the time", "no anxiety - at ease".

FURTHER ADVANTAGES WERE LISTED BY THE UNOPERATED GROUP OF MtF's

"breasts developed" x13, "increased hip size" x3, "waist narrowed" x2, "more passive" x2, "more relaxed" x2, "less aggressive", "face softer" x2, "skin texture improved" x9, "hair improved" x5, "body hair better" x2, "mood more stable" x2, "happy" x7, "contentment" x2, "feeling complete", "steady psychological improvement", "eyes brighter", "body shape better" x3, "filling out", "calmer" x5, "feel more female daily", "nicer", "care more for others", "mistaken for a woman when dressed as a man", "hope".

Summary on other matters on evaluation thus far:

At the time of this questionnaire there were far fewer female to male TS's coming forward than MtF's, although the ratio is closing. It is thought that the problems of phalloplasty deter many FtM's from seeking surgery or coming forward to the G.I.C.'s for treatment. This ratio was thought to be 1:4, FtM to MtF.

There were a total of 9 FtM's against a total of 93 MtF's, a ratio of 1 to 9.

Part of the reason for this is that the FtM's seem less "clubbish", and tend not to use the advantages of joining groups.

The 8 MtF's who state they will not have surgery took this decision for the following reasons: medical advice (in 2 cases), a heart condition (1 case), couldn't bear to leave loving wife (1), family, business and social reasons (1). They formed an older average age group, range (31 to 74), average age 56.8 Years, against 42 in the other groups.

Of those FtM's who remained undecided, 3 said it was because they were married, 2 because they were not convinced that the surgery was very good.

Nobody described herself then as transgenderist rather than "TS", which is a non-surgical option some choose in 1992, the life style rather than the body image being the most important difficulty they have.

DO YOU SUFFER FROM ANY OTHER MEDICAL CONDITIONS
Among the MtF's 93 respondents the complaints listed were (incidence in brackets): anxiety (1), arthritis - showed up when started Androcur (1), arthritis - rheumatoid (1), asthma (2), Candida infection - post op (1), colitis (mild), gastric pain - which cleared up when gender treatment started (1), gastric ulcers (1), gout - mild (1), hay fever (8), heart problems (2 - 1 heart attack), hiatus hernia, haemorrhoids (1), hypertension (5), Ménière's disease (1), Migraine (1), Myxoedema (1), Psoriasis ((2) (of chest 1, of arms 1), Psychological illness (1), Sinusitis (1) skin rashes (1).

Among the FtM replies the following were reported:
Asthma, cataracts - both eyes, hypertension, multiple sclerosis, Stokes Adams syndrome.

CONCLUSION: An 8.6% Incidence of hay fever seems high, (there must be a lot of sneezing Trannies!)
It would seem that various forms of illness may be attributed to the actual diagnosis … stress, depression, anxiety, gastric disturbance.

DO YOU HAVE ANY ALLERGIES?
Aspirin, Anti-tetanus serum, aubergines, Caffeine, cat and dog fur, cereals, cheese, chocolate, coffee, cocaine, cow milk, creosote, cucumber, Elastoplast, grass pollen, hair spray solvent, hair, hay fever, 4x house dust, Oris root, Paracetamol, 3x Penicillin, 5x pollen, raw eggs, seafood, 2x soap, solvent in wet paint, tobacco, 2x wheat, white bread, wool, 2x yeast

CONCLUSION:
There is a high incidence and range of allergies reported.
Additional information from the respondents was that:
1 reported an allergic response to Premarin, after 3 days use, which ceased when Premarin discontinued in 3 more days. Diane was prescribed with no such problem.
1 reported a violent reaction to Androcur, which cleared up when it was discontinued.

Many report gastric disturbance when they were on Stilboesterol. Premarin is now the medication of choice in most prescribers.

IF POST OP HAS YOUR DOSE RATE BEEN CHANGED?

Sustanol 250 replaced with Sustanol 100 in 2 cases.

Testorol replaced by Mesterolone after hysterectomy in 1 case.

Premarin dose is usually reported to have been reduced from 7.5 mg a day to 2.5 mg a day, more than half the post op's report this. Others state dose rate halved, and in one case quartered, in one case Oestrogens were stopped altogether, and in one there was no dose rate reduction. 3 were found to still be on Androcur post-op.

HOW MANY YEARS HAVE YOU BEEN ON HORMONES?

'Female' hormones

(A) Premarin:

16 < 1 year.	3 > 4 years.	2 > 9 years.	1 >18 years.
9 > 1 years.	1 > 5 years.	3 >10 years.	
7 > 2 years.	4 > 6 years.	1 >11 years.	
9 > 3 years.	1 > 7 years.	1 >13 years.	

i.e. 14/56 Had taken Premarin more than 5 years.

(B) Androcur:

This is an anti-androgen, normally prescribed in conjunction with Premarin. It need not, one feels, continue post op. In at least three cases we found it was.

4 < 1 year.   1 > 1 years.   1 > 2 years.   1 > 3 years. 1 > 5 years.

(C) Ethinyloestradiol:

The prescriber has largely replaced this by Premarin.

3 > 1 year.   1 > 2 years.   1 5 years.   1 10 years.   1 27 years.

(D) Stilboestrol:

This has largely been replaced by the prescriber by Premarin, since it has a higher incidence of gastric disturbances etc.

2 > 1 year.   1 > 3 years.   1 20 years.

'Male' hormones.

(A) Sustanon 250 i/m monthly:

1 > 5 years.   1 > 11 years.   1 > 13 years.

(B) Testorol: 2 > 1 year.   1 > 3 years. 1 > 13 years.

(C) Restandol: 1 > 1 year.

(D) Mestranol 1 < 1 year.

A number failed to reply to these questions.

BEFORE HORMONES WERE PRESCRIBED DID YOU HAVE THE FOLLOWING?

There were 89/102 prescribed hormones. All relevant replied y/n. They may, in some cases, have made errors in recollection, and some of this preliminary work will hopefully have been done by the G.P. who referred them.

Blood test:	34 yes = 38.2%
Physical examination:	37 yes = 41.6%
Medical history taken:	57 yes = 69%
Blood pressure taken:	43 yes = 51%
Blood test for endocrine/hormone level:	23 yes = 25.8%
Chromosome analysis:	18 yes = 20.2%
Buccal smear:	8 yes = 9%

ONCE ON HORMONES, WERE THE FOLLOWING CHECKED?

Blood hormone levels:	19 yes = 21.3%
Blood pressure:	50 yes = 56.2%
Weight increase or loss:	28 yes = 31.5%

COMMENT: If these results are given correctly by the patients a good deal of preventative and investigative work is being ignored by the G.I.C.'s, apart from the loss to research and scientific method, we feel that blood pressure should always be monitored, at least 3 monthly.

IF YOUR HORMONE THERAPY WAS CHANGED, HAS THIS BROUGHT ABOUT AN IMPROVEMENT TO YOUR LIFE?

11 Replied yes, 10 no change, 2 not improved.

IF SO WHAT?

MtF: "Androcur allows 21 days on 7 days off Oestrogens in cyclic regime, also gave dramatic hair loss on face and body, and made me more feminine looking".

FtM: "weight returned to normal, acne cleared up, no need for tablets", "Lowered blood pressure", "breakthrough bleeding stopped."

IF POST OP HAS YOUR RESPONSE TO HORMONES IMPROVED?

10/18 MtF said yes =55.6%

"breast growth better" x2, "less unwanted hair on arms and legs", "no nausea now" x2, "can take less medication", "need less electrolysis" x2, "more feminization" x2, "happiness", "calmer", "less facial hair" x3, "figure improved".

HAVE YOU BEEN REFERRED TO A G.I.C.?
(18 Gave no answer, 70 "yes" replies given 14 "no's"):
Of post ops (23), 13 had had referral to a G.I.C., (one had closed),
and of the post ops (in both directions) 6 had hormones supplied via
G.I.C.'s & 12 via their G.P.
A number of post op's had not seen a G.I.C., and were c/o their G.P.
only.
So of the 102 respondents 70% c/o a G.I.C.

DOES G.I.C. OR G.P. PRESCRIBE YOUR HORMONES NOW?
32 Said G.I.C. prescribed their hormones (=30%)
61 said their G.P. prescribed them. (=60%)
Of these about half said this was under direction from G.I.C. or a
psychiatrist.

PLEASE LIST ANY OTHER TYPES OF DRUG THAT MAY NOT HAVE BEEN MEDICALLY PRESCRIBED:
"Alcohol - to forget", "alcohol due to depression",
Mineral and vitamin supplements, Vitamin C (x3), Vit E, Halibut oil,
Vita (x2),
Royal jelly, Zinc (for healing), Calendula, Arnica, Biotin, Calcium tabs.
Betacarotin (Vit A).

HAVE YOU EVER HAD THE FOLLOWING? (IF "YES"- DID IT HELP?)
Psychiatry: 72% had, 40% said it was helpful.
Psychotherapy: 28% had, 64% said it did not help.
Social skills: 18% had, 64% said it was helpful.

HAVE YOU TRIED TO GIVE UP TRANSSEXUALISM?
62% had tried, none found it possible.
Have you had:
Behaviour therapy?   4 had, none found it helped.
Shock treatment?   5 had, none found it helped.
Corrective psychology?   3 had, none found it helped.

Have you tried other methods?
(a) Co-counselling   1 had
(b) hypnotherapy   1 had
(c) unspecified   1 had
None worked to stop TS, but "a and b" helped to handle the problems.

POST-OP GROUP:

Did you have the following follow-ups? (There were 23 post ops)

12 had follow up check ups = 52%. 83% said this helped.

Psychotherapy? 6 had = 26%, 1 said it helped.

Psychiatry? 9 had = 39% 3 said it helped.

Social help? 2 had = 8.7% No comments.

Counselling? 7 had = 30% all said it helped.

Help finding work? 2 had. No comments.

COMMENT: It would seem far more needs to be done post op in counselling especially.

HAVE YOU HAD ANY COSMETIC SURGERY?

17 people had cosmetic surgery - Not including gender confirmation surgery, and breast surgery. (All were MtF). The operations listed were: 8x rhinoplasty (nose jobs), 2x face lifts (private), 2x chin reshaping, 1 ear surgery, 1 Adam's apple reduction, 1 tattoo removed, 1 orthodontic surgery. 1 nostrils reshaped, 1 narrowing of nose bridge.

HAVE YOU HAD ELECTROLYSIS?

(Sample 91, remainder were 11 M to F).

65 have had electrolysis = 71%, 9 made no reply, 17 say they have not, 21 replied as to did it help? 13 Said yes = 62%.

Other forms of depilation:

6 x had waxing, 2 x used Immac to arms and legs, 1 x had thermolysis to face & chest

1 had Depilex - said it was no good.

HAVE YOU HAD SPEECH THERAPY?

Of replies 30 had = 37%

8 of 37 said it helped them.

DO YOU HAVE VOICE PROBLEMS?

Of 91 MtF's 44/80 said they had voice problems = 55%.

Of 9 FtM's 1 said he had a voice problem =11.1%.

HOW WELL DO YOU MANAGE WITH SPEECH?

Of 102 questionnaires returned, 9 gave no answer, 93 answered.

Of these: 34 managed well = 36%.,41 average= 44%, 17 managed badly= 18%, 1 variable.

DO YOU DO WEIGHT TRAINING? (FtM)'S
2/9 does weight lifting. No MtF's said they did.

DO YOU HAVE A PARTNER?
Of 102: 42 said they had = 41%, 52 said no = 51%,   9 no reply.   4 said still with their wife.

(A number remain with their wife or ex-wife as "sisters".)

IS S/HE HAPPY WITH RESULTS OF YOUR HORMONE THERAPY?
Of 102:   38 answered   Yes, 4 x No, 1 x Not aware   1 x Indifferent
The partners were marked by some as "he"= 6; "she"= 12, not stated = 16, and "TS" by 1.
We feel that an awkward question has been avoided by many.

ARE YOU INTERESTED IN YOUR GENERAL HEALTH?
There were 59 replies, 57 yes, 2 no.

ARE YOU OBSESSED WITH YOUR GENERAL HEALTH?
There were 60 replies, 3 yes, 57 no.
We wondered if there might be an admitted hypochondria in these three.

DID D.S.S. HELP WITH COST OF YOUR ELECTROLYSIS?
There were 77 replies, 76 no and 1 yes. This help is very much the exception not the rule.

WORK? There were 86 replies.
Employees x 2, self employed x 20,   retired x 17   unemployed x 13
employers x 3   students x 2   housewife x 1
This represents only 15% who see themselves as out of work.

IF UNEMPLOYED, HOW LONG?
There were 18 replies to years out of work:

4 x	1 year,	1 x	8 yrs.
2 x	between 1 & 2 years	5 x	5 yrs.
2 x	2 yrs.	1 x	10 yrs.
1 x	3 yrs.	1 x	18yrs.
1 x	4 yrs.		

This gives a mean of 4.5 Years of this group

DID YOU OBTAIN WORK DURING YOUR FIRST TWO YEARS OF CHANGE OVER?
There were 44 replies, 29 yes, 15 no.

SINCE HORMONE THERAPY HOW WERE YOU?
There were 80 replies. 77 were happier, 2 were unhappy, 1 no change
Since change over were you?....
There were 52 replies: 44 were happier, 8 no change
Post op's (23)
Since op were you? ...
There were 15 replies: 13 were happier, 2 no change.

HAVE YOU HAD ANY COMPLICATIONS FROM HORMONES?
There were 83 replies: 75 said no, 8 said yes.

(All went on to say this was put right by dose or medication change.)

SEXUALITY - WOULD YOU DESCRIBE YOURSELF AS:
There were 92/102 replies:

Of these

heterosexual 42 = 45%   asexual 29 = 27%   bisexual 14 = 16%
lesbian   5 = 6%   celibate 1 = 1%

Replies inferred that in the main sexual preference is seen from the gender of the respondent, rather than from the point of view of genetic sex. Thus a transexed person, MtF will often describe herself as a lesbian if she is sexually attracted to other women, or as heterosexual if her preferred partner be a man. A number who remained with their wives said they were lesbians; their wives might not agree. What is clear is that sexual preference is across the spectrum, although there are large numbers of TS's who see themselves as asexual (32%). This does all help to dispel the myth that the TS are such because of sex rather than gender.

RELATIONSHIPS - WOULD YOU DESCRIBE YOURSELF AS:
There were 85 replies:

single   35 = 41%   divorced   23 = 27%   partnered 14 = 16%
married 10 = 16%   widowed   2 = 3%   separated   1 = 1%
This means that 24/85 = 28% see themselves in a relationship; so implies that 72% are alone.

DO YOU SEEK A PARTNER?
1 any, 5 have, 27 yes, 62/99 no.

This implies that 2/3 of transexed people are unattached and not seeking a partner.

ARE ANY OF YOUR FAMILY TV/TS/GAY/BISEXUAL/NONE?

There were 93 replies, 86/93 "none's" = 92%, i.e. 1 in 10 "yes":

These were: 1 bisexual, 1 gay uncle, 1 gay cousin ,1 "father had sex problems" = 4/93 = 4.3%,

A below expected average % for the general population. Also, there was 1 transvestite, and 2 transsexuals "in the family". These were not listed as immediate relatives, but this figure of 3/93 = 3.2%, is remarkable. It could as much imply a nature aetiology as a nurture one, and without the exact relationships and a larger sample it is hard to evaluate. No work done so far has evidenced a strong familial factor in incidence of transsexualism, though some intersexed conditions may be genetically linked.

FAMILY REACTION TO YOUR CHANGE OVER:

(a)   97 replies. Estimated reaction given as:
26 hostile (includes 3 wives),   13 negative   16 neutral
39 accept ("children", "some", "daughter", "not brother", "not sister"),
3 happy

(b) *family reaction to you post-op (32 replies):*
5 hostile   5 neutral   16 accept   6 happy

(c) *society's reaction to you now (73 replies):*
1 hostile   4 negative   19 neutral   35 accept   14 happy

SELF ESTIMATE BEFORE CHANGED OVER:

68 replies: 16 hostile, 2 accepting 30 negative 5 happy 15 neutral

Self estimate after change over:
65 replies   3 negative   5 neutral   17 accepting   40 happy

Self estimate post-op
25 replies given from possible 23 post operative sample.
Some live gender adapted with only breast surgery, or non-full gender reassignment surgery which may account for this anomaly.
1 neutral   3 accepting   21 happy.

IF CHANGED OVER ARE YOU A ... ?

"Typical man"   4x (3 = undecided MtF's + 1 = a post op F to M)
"Liberated man"   6x (all FtM TS's, = 5 post op + 1 pre op)
"Feminist"   8x (MtF TS's = 7 pre op + 1 post op)
"I am not typical"   2x (FtM)
"I am just an individual"   1x (MtF)
"Typical woman"   58x
(including 1 who put "professional woman"+1 who put "elderly woman")

HAVE YOU GIVEN UP MOST OF YOUR ORIGINAL INTERESTS?

There were 81 replies:

"no"= 60 = (post op's 15 + 45 pre op's)

"yes"= 17 = (post op's 3 + 14 pre op's)

Pre op's: = 15/23 - 65% did not give up their original interests.

Post op's = 45/79 - 57% did not give up their original interests.

Additionally were: (3 "same") + 1 "most")

No FtM's say they have changed their interests; on investigation they were never interested in traditionally feminine things.

The MtF's appear to be more stereotypical than the FtM's in reacting against gender conditioning, which often resulted in them taking up activity and interests which they felt society expected of them before change over. This causes a reaction against 'masculine' activities and interests, which many women, born female now do - against what is expected of women and girls. The male to female transsexual often seems to portray an outmoded version of womanhood by being super feminine in dress and activity.

The restrictions in men's dress codes and expected activity can probably be blamed for this over stereotypical reaction, and the uncharitable disdain for them felt and expressed by more unenlightened feminists.

IS YOUR PARTNER THE ORIGINAL ONE?

There were 42 replies:

"yes"= 25 pre op's + 4 post op's = total 29/42 of replies;

This means of the replies 69% were with their original partners, some post op's were still married.

"No"= 4 pre op's + 9 post op's = total 13/42 of replies; This implies that 9/23 = 39% of post op's had split from their original partners.

IF YOU HAVE LEFT YOUR ORIGINAL PARTNER, IS YOUR PRESENT PARTNER THE SAME SEX AS THE ORIGINAL ONE?

"Yes"= 23 pre op's + 7 post op's = total 30/35 of replies;

"No"= 2 pre op's + 3 post op's = total 5/35 of replies:

There were 10 post op replies, so 86% of them retained the same sexual preference as before surgery, and most of these would describe themselves as lesbians.

CONCLUSION: Surgery does not necessarily change the sexual preference. After surgery, sex is described as being different. Many report that orgasms are possible.

DURING YOUR ASSESSMENT PERIOD WERE YOU?

N.H.S. or private? There were 90 replies.: 17 were private = 19%, 73 were N.H.S. = 81%.If post op was surgery N.H.S. or private?

There were 23 postoperative replies: 19 were N.H.S. during assessment and 5 private. 8 were N.H.S. for surgery and 15 private.

This means that due to the long waiting lists 10/23 elected to transfer to private medicine for surgery. The surgeons are the same and the facilities in the N.H.S. are as good as in private medicine, yet 43% opt not to wait any longer. There is a 3 to 1 ratio of private surgery to N.H.S. This also shows a trend towards having N.H.S. psychiatry and private surgery.

Respondents were asked to indicate other surgery carried out on N.H.S.:
Tattoo removal, breast correction, colostomy. Most plastic surgery was done privately.

CONCLUSIONS: The response to hormones should take into account other conditions, individual response and their side effects that are disadvantageous. An holistic approach is desirable.

Drug companies and physicians, psychiatrists and endocrinologists should work together to monitor and provide entirely suitable drug regimes which are properly monitored for both pre- and post-operative TS's, while all side effects should be reported. Blood pressure should be taken three monthly by the G.P. or the G.I.C. Liaison should be improved. Follow-up studies are entirely necessary.

At the time of this questionnaire, there were far fewer female to male TS's coming forward, than male to female, although the ratio is closing. In this questionnaire, there was a ratio of 9:93 FtM : MtF. Part of the reason for this is that the FtM's are less 'clubbish' and tend not to use the advantages of joining groups.

It is also thought that the problems of phalloplasty deter many FtM's from seeking surgery, or coming forward to the G.I.C's for treatment. This ratio is thought to be 1:4 FtM : MtF.

For MtF's expectations of surgery are probably too high.

71.   Parents and their Gender Dysphoric/ Transexed Child.

So-called "Primary Transsexuals" do tend to present earlier than "Secondary Transsexuals" do. As children, pre-puberty, they may state categorically to a mother who believes she has a son, "I am a girl", "I want to play with girls", "I want to go to a girl's school", "My name is Roberta", "When I grow up I will be a lady like you Mummy".

All children experiment whilst finding and establishing their own gender identity. This is part of normal development and play. A boy who tries on a dress, or a girl who likes football, usually means nothing, and should not cause a parent, or the child, concerns.

When, however, a child is drawing a great deal of consistent attention to her, or his, gender discomfort, then there may be a long term problem which needs to be addressed. Often a transexed boy is secretive about his feeling that he should be girl. He might feel confused and ashamed. He quickly learns that sissies are ridiculed and become playground victims. Other children seem to feel uncomfortable around them, reinforced by their parents', playmates' or teachers' phallocratic attitudes. Soon a child learns which games he 'should' - and which he cannot even want to - play, and which playmates she, or he, can have.

For tomboys it does seem easier, and of course few tomboys want to be boys or become men. Girl power or liberation means a girl can be open in challenging traditional values about what a girl can or can not want to be or do. A Dad will feel proud if his daughter plays football, or goes to the match with him. Both parents would generally feel concerned or angry if their ten year old boy parades around in heels, pushing a pram, or experiments with makeup.

Gentleness or sensitivity should not be confused with femininity. Both boys and girls will I believe be more liberated if they can explore the traditionally 'masculine' or 'feminine' components in their personality. Exaggerated effeminacy is more often an indicator that a boy might be homosexual (but so can his being a bully and thuggish if he is trying to over compensate and to hide this).

It is important that both parents allow their child to talk of their thoughts and ideas to them, that they use empathy, that they listen and do not talk at the child. They need to try to learn gently what is in their child's mind, rather than beat them for being 'naughty' if found 'dressed up' or upset about being a boy and not a girl, or vice versa.

If a change over were to be commenced before puberty - using hormones to stimulate secondary sexual characteristics of the desired gender, then of course the change-over would be physically much more acceptable. No facial hair, natural breasts, no broken voice, would really help a boy to develop convincingly into a woman.

A transexed 'female' child will hate her breasts, periods, dresses and skirts and all those 'terrible frills' girls often have to wear. Most children in this position find it very hard to articulate what they feel; it is easier to wish or to dream. To talk to parents is far harder than it should be, for what the child needs to state is 'against' even a very good parent, in that it is tremendously challenging. Some parents simply are not up to it; some are more enlightened or courageous.

The group *Mermaids*, at BM MERMAIDS, London WC1N 3XX, is a family support group for parents with children with long standing gender identity issues.

Much of the original work done with gender dysphoric children started in the Netherlands. In the UK it is estimated that there are at least 600 children who have shown they need help from their parents and a GIC.

The Gender Identity Development Clinic, which was originally at St. George's Hospital Tooting under the direction of Dr. Domenico Di Cegli now, works from the Portman Clinic, NW3. This is the world's first specific unit for treating gender dysphoric children. It is able to function using informed consent and full parental involvement. I know from some of their clients that it seems to them to be over-conservative in offering hormones etc., however it is reasonable that nothing irreversible be done, in case, at a later date, it seems to have been a mistake. Guidelines are being considered as this book is being written.

The NHS has traditionally avoided interventions using hormones, except on intersexed children, until recent years. The impression I have from of my originally intersexed clients is that the sex was chosen based on pragmatic parameters, but more to satisfy the parents, than necessarily to suit the child and his or her gender identity. This is not surprising since gender identity was seen as having its origin wholly in nurture (as a post-Freudian view of gender identity as a function in the strictly behaviourist sense of upbringing). Much of psychiatry is still influenced by such models, which have been profoundly challenged. Some still continue to adopt only the view that the greatest influence on identity is psychological, not biological. It is surprising that, as doctors of medicine, a greater emphasis on a biological rationale, is not in place and apparent in their training or thinking.

A doctor or midwife is put on the spot at a birth. There an overwhelming pressure at this moment to answer the vital question first asked, "is it a boy or a girl?"

The answer "yes" will not do! Everyone wants to know at once which it is, there are "only two choices", and so interventions have often been made before the child's gender preference is in any respect considered. Perhaps a case for caution in terms of surgery would be worth making here.

With apparently clearly sexually defined (physically) patients the NHS is still quite cautious about providing surgical interventions before the patient is 21, let alone under 18. However, cases known to this author have been helped as early as the 1970's and the resulting women seem very much happier (and more convincing) than many of their late-starter sisters.

This early diagnosis and appropriate intervention also avoids the possible pitfalls of marriage, an established role and job in the 'wrong' gender and all the untangling that has to take place for the late-presenting cases. The Unit at the Tavistock works with co-workers and parents and school authorities that have co-operated with adolescent TS patients/pupils. At last child psychiatry and psychology are beginning to address and understand some of the problems.

At my son's own school there was a girl who insisted that she was a boy. She played football, cricket, rugby, wore boys' clothes, and was a far better, happier individual once this was allowed. The boys respected her/him and the girls at least got used to him.

There are hormone retarding substances (such as Leuprorelin = Postat S.R. injections, and the nasal sprays Suprecur and Suprefact) that can delay puberty. These have been used in the Netherlands with considerable success in avoiding the pitfalls of an inappropriate puberty in children who are clearly gender dysphoric. This is only possible with parental consent. For the new Mr. or Miss the outlook need not be bleak - given these parental and other backups. The nasal sprays seem to be less effective and there have been complaints of nasal irritation possibly caused by them. Leuprorelin is injected once a month i/m, and seems to work well with few apparent side effects. However a clinician has to ensure (with a bone scan) that growth has completed, as they are LHRH analogues.

I now include, unabridged, a Document from GIRES on Families.

215

72. Supporting the Families of Adult Gender Dysphoric and Transsexual People.

The Gender Identity Research and Education (GIRES) supports families in which a member experiences gender dysphoria or transsexualism. So far, it has directly helped 160 people by providing  individual advice sessions, telephone contact and workshops, in collaboration with Mermaids and Depend that enable families to meet others with relevant experience. GIRES believes that the information below would be helpful to other families dealing with these issues and to the organisations that wish to support them.

GENDER IDENTITY and TRANSSEXUALISM

Family members faced with issues of gender dysphoria and transsexualism usually seek an answer to the same burning questions: how has this occurred?

What did I do wrong? The following information should help them by explaining what is understood about the development of gender dysphoria, and relieving them of any sense of being guilty for the way it has developed. Male and female characteristics depend on two factors: sex and gender.

'Sex' describes our physical structure, including external appearance, internal organs and brain, which all differ between males and females. There are two different aspects to gender: 'gender identity' describes the inner sense of knowing that we are boys or girls, and later men or women; 'gender role' describes how we behave in society.

Even though we now live in a more equal society, boys and girls are still expected to dress differently from each other and, possibly, enjoy different kinds of games. Each is expected to have rather different interests and different groups of friends.

Typically, sex, gender identity and gender role are consistent with each other. So, we tend to think of human beings as falling into two distinct categories: boys and men, who are 'male'; girls and women who are 'female'.

As soon as the sex of a baby is apparent, it is assumed that the gender identity matches. However, people vary greatly and it should not be surprising that, occasionally, a few individuals experience a mismatch. The way they look on the outside doesn't fit how they feel inside. The way they are expected to behave may be quite different from the way they actually want to behave. This causes a feeling of intense discomfort, which is described as 'gender dysphoria' (dysphoria means unhappiness). This condition is increasingly understood to have its origins before birth. Research studies indicate that a small part of the baby's brain develops in opposition to the sex of the rest of its body.

This predisposes the baby to a future mismatch between gender identity and sex.

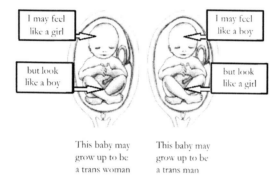

This baby may grow up to be a trans woman

This baby may grow up to be a trans man

As the individual grows through childhood, adolescence and on into adulthood, the discomfort may become extreme. Even so, many will continue to strive to live and behave according to the gender role that society expects of them.

However, for some, the stress of their situation may become so intolerable that medical help is sought to enable the individual concerned to undergo 'transition', that is, to live according to the opposite gender role, and to have treatment, usually including hormone medication and surgery, to bring the body more closely in line with the underlying gender identity.

Those who seek this treatment may be referred to as transsexual people or trans men (female to male) and trans women (male to female). This treatment is very successful in giving trans people the feeling of harmony that they seek. Gender dysphoria has nothing to do with

217

sexuality, that is, whether a person is gay/lesbian or straight. The sexual orientation of trans people, as in the population generally, may be towards men, women or both. In any case, the trans person is likely to be unsure of future orientation until gender-confirming surgery has been completed. It may remain same; it may change.

Gender dysphoria is not a mental illness, although the condition can cause great stress in the lives of the individuals concerned and their families.

Trans people's rights are now recognised in law. They will be able to obtain a Gender Recognition Certificate, leading to a new birth certificate, which will help to prevent discrimination against them. They will also be allowed to marry in their newly recognised gender.

However, as a consequence of society's lack of understanding and care, trans people often suffer a great deal, just at a time when they most need support.

Many find that their families reject them. Sometimes, despite being protected by employment law, they are made to feel very uncomfortable at work, as well as elsewhere.

It takes great courage for trans people to reveal their true gender identities. They deserve respect and understanding.

FAMILIES' NEED FOR SUPPORT

Families' support for gender dysphoric and transsexual people is vital.

Poor support has been shown to make it more likely that trans people will regret their transition to a new gender role, post surgery.

However, families themselves also need support if they are to be able to help their trans loved one. Families' own needs are often neglected by the gender identity clinics that treat trans people, even deliberately. Family members are subjected to extreme stress, especially partners. Typical reactions to the news of a loved one's gender dysphoria, especially if it has already been confirmed as transsexualism, include,

- shock
- guilt
- pain and grief
- betrayal
- losing control
- anger

- embarrassment and shame
- fear, for self and loved one
- possibly religious concerns

In cases where the transition occurs late in the trans person's life, it often involves partners/spouses and children, which greatly aggravates relationship difficulties. The partner/spouse may feel betrayed, especially if told late in the decision-making process. If the trans person has children, the partner/spouse will be deeply concerned about the effect on them. The partner/spouse may be deeply concerned about being labelled lesbian or gay and, perhaps, having to face the problems of a sexually unfulfilling relationship. Nonetheless, for some families, there may also be relief that a mystery has been solved. They may, for many years, have wondered and worried about some inexplicable ways in which their loved one has behaved.

Almost invariably, families will not know the best way to respond. Their initial shock and resistance to the idea of transsexualism are understandable reactions. They do need to be convinced that this is the right path for the person they love. However, the search for easy solutions is usually fruitless. It is unlikely, and perhaps unsafe, for an adult trans person to change his or her mind and revert to the initial gender role and presentation. Trying to persuade the trans person to delay transition may be very harmful. Very probably, the trans person has already reached crisis point before telling the family. Once the trans person begins to tell people about the intention to begin transition, it is impossible to keep it a secret.

In their anxiety, families often fail to recognise that the trans person and his or her love for other members of the family remain unchanged. The trans person will be acutely aware of the pain that this situation causes other family members and feeling deep sorrow about that. However, family members need to be aware that the trans person is driven by an overwhelming need to live in accordance with his/her innate gender identity, while remaining reliant on the family's acceptance, listening, understanding, advice, support and, above all, love.

Nonetheless, it is true that trans individuals may become entirely self-focused through the transition process. Society often places major obstacles in their way and overcoming them requires determination.

They may feel that have spent their entire lives pleasing everyone else; now it's their turn. They will want their families to be happy for them. Sometimes, they will have difficulty in understanding why their families are not enthusiastic about this transformation.

ISSUES TO BE FACED
It is helpful for trans people and their families to look realistically at the daunting range of issues to be dealt with during the transition process:

- Psychiatric assessment to confirm the diagnosis
- Understanding a vast amount of new information about gender identity and transsexualism
- Obtaining funds for treatment, NHS or private
- Carefully informing all who need to know
- Undergoing the real life experience that is a mandatory precursor to surgical treatment, which requires living in the new gender role full-time
- Handling relationships
- Maintaining access to own children
- Certificate of gender confirmation treatment for use if challenged in using toilets or other gender segregated facilities.
- Statutory declaration of new identity to use in obtaining new documents
- Medication
- Employment
- Pension provisions
- Entitlement to state benefits
- Entertainment and social activities
- Media intrusion
- Transphobic crime
- Legal support to deal with extreme problems
- Crisis, even rape, support
- Counselling
- Artificial body parts
- Clothing, footwear and wigs
- Behaviour and deportment
- Cosmetics
- Hair removal

- Speech therapy
- Surgery: genitals, gonads, breast, trachea, face

The list of documents and records that the trans person has to change is also very long:

- Driving licence
- Passport
- Degrees and other qualifications
- GP and other doctors
- Other medical services e.g. Dentist, Optician
- Tax and National Insurance
- Personnel records at work
- Pension records
- Benefits Agency
- Job Centre
- Bank and Building Society
- Personal and household insurance policies
- Mortgage
- H.P. Agreements
- Credit cards
- Utilities: Gas, Electricity, Water, Phone
- Council Tax
- Electoral Roll
- Club memberships
- Birth certificate, after grant of a gender recognition certificate, (commencing 2005)
- ID Cards (commencing whenever the proposed new legislation comes into effect)

In this complex and changing situation, the inevitable stress, for trans people and their families, severely inhibits communication, making it even harder for all of them to sustain an effective relationship.

Very often, the importance of surgery is given exaggerated importance, by trans people and their families, in comparison with the many other factors above that have to be dealt with successfully to ensure a happy life for the trans person. However, for most trans people, surgery is essential and it is very expensive. Many trans people cannot afford private treatment. The NHS makes only limited funds available for this treatment. Funding priorities are set locally by the strategic health authorities and primary care trusts.

Waiting lists for surgery, or indeed for other medical treatment can be long.

Families, as well as trans people, need to be aware of the surgical options:

a - MtF (Trans Woman):

i - orchidectomy   ii - penectomy   iii - vaginoplasty
iv - clitoroplasty
v - mammoplasty   vi - tracheal shave   vii - facial feminising

b - FtM (Trans Man):

i - mastectomy   ii - hysterectomy
iii - oophorectomy   iv - metoidioplasty
v - phalloplasty   vi - penile implant

Hormone treatment is likely to affect the trans person's libido (sex-drive).

In trans women (MtF), the effect of the hormones (anti-androgens and estrogens) is likely to reduce libido. In trans men (FtM), it is likely to be increased by the hormones (testosterone). Both trans women and trans men can experience orgasm postoperatively.

HOW TO SUPPORT FAMILIES

The support that best helps families includes:

* Providing information on gender dysphoria and transsexualism
* Promoting mutual insight, so that:
  * family members understand the trans person's reality
  * the trans person understands the family's bewilderment and sense of loss
* Providing opportunities to share feelings with others in similar position
* Encouraging realism and optimism

GIRES can provide a literature pack that deals with:

* a full scientific explanation of gender dysphoria and transsexualism
* the support groups that can help trans people and family members; these are voluntary organisations with relevant expertise; confidentiality is assured for those who contact them; GIRES can provide a list of these organisations, which gives information on the services they offer and how to contact them. Families often seek guidance about the best way to respond. The advice that seems most valuable to them is:

1 Don't ignore the problem and hope that it will go away.
2 Welcome discussion with your family member whenever he or she wishes to talk about gender identity issues.
3 Allow yourself to become convinced as rapidly as you can that you should and will unconditionally accept your loved one's decision about his or her gender identity and give them your support; do this in days, ideally, in weeks if possible, rather than months.
4 It will then be best for you and for your loved one if you:
   a. respect the fundamental right of your family member to be true to him or herself.
   b. accept that living in accordance with the core gender identity is now absolutely essential for him or her.
   c. are realistic rather than pessimistic about the many problems that you both will have to face.
   d. take positive action so that you influence events rather than allow them to drive you.
      i. resist the notion that you are to blame or in any way responsible for your loved one's decision.
      ii. share the news with at least one other person whom you can rely on to respect the need for confidentiality, until you and your family member are ready to share it more widely.
      iii. contact a support group.
      iv. if you still find the stress too much to handle, obtain professional help, perhaps via your GP.
      v. provide a safe haven where your loved one will feel protected from an often hostile outside world.
      vi. use the name and also the pronouns that your loved one prefers: "she", "he", "her", "him", "hers", "his"; both of you must expect that you will, initially, often get this wrong.
      vii. offer advice tactfully, e.g. on clothes, make-up, etc.
      viii. learn about gender identity development from literature, articles, books and, if you can, internet sites set up by reputable organisations
      ix. learn the language used in your loved one's new world: e.g. "sex", "gender identity", "gender role", "male", "female", "masculine", "feminine", "gender dysphoria", "transsexualism", "transition", "trans man", "trans woman"
      x. appreciate that your loved one is having to explore a new

world of trans people and those that serve their special needs.

xi. gradually inform others who need to know, especially family members.

xii. become confident and knowledgeable enough to challenge ignorance and intolerance in others.

xiii. look for ways to help others in a similar position.

What will be unhelpful is to:

1 continue refusing to believe what your loved one is telling you.

2 try to make things like they previously were.

3 keep the news a complete secret from everyone.

4 become antagonistic towards the professionals who are trying to help your loved one.

5 allow yourself to believe that there is nothing positive you can do.

6 expect only bad consequences from your loved one's decision to have treatment for his or her gender dysphoria

Major issues often arise concerning children. Parents may wish for help in informing their children about gender identity and transsexual issues.

For this purpose, GIRES can provide explanations, set at two levels: one for pre-teens, the other for teenagers. These documents are also useful for schools that have to deal with such issues, because either pupils have trans parents or pupils are themselves gender dysphoric.

In some cases, parents may separate, with one of them having custody of the children. The parent having custody may deny the other parent reasonable access to the children. In such a case, a court hearing may ensue. GIRES provides literature to help the trans parent in such circumstances.

WORKSHOPS FOR FAMILIES

The workshops that GIRES has run, in 9 major cities throughout the UK, allowed participants to share their experiences and put questions to the trans people and family members that made up the team of presenters. Each workshop, lasting three hours, took place on Saturday afternoons when it was reasonably certain that the trans people and their families would be free to attend. Participants included partners, children, parents, siblings, friends and also trans people, but only if they attended with their families. Allowing trans people to attend without their family members would have focused discussion on the problems that trans people face, at the expense of spending time on the vital issue of family relationships. Although a number of counsellors and others asked to attend the workshops, no spectators were allowed in order to ensure that participants felt free to talk openly to people directly sharing similar experiences.

The ground rules that GIRES set creates a safe and supportive atmosphere. Everyone should be treated with respect. Confidentiality should be assured.

Assurances should be given that no information will be passed on to those providing treatment. Family members should be warned not to attempt to interfere in treatment. For part of the time, participants are divided into three smaller groups: trans people partners, parents and siblings. Each group is facilitated by an appropriate team member. This enables participants to concentrate on issues specific to their personal situation, and it greatly facilitates discussion in a safe environment.

The evaluation forms completed by participants showed that they had been helped to understand and accept their loved one's condition Their comments also showed that they had obtained reassurance through:

1 knowing "I'm not the only one"
2 companionship and sharing
3 ability to talk openly
4 hugs with other participants

Another important benefit of bringing families together is that it enables them, by exchanging telephone numbers and e-mail, to network after the workshop is over.

In presenting the workshops, GIRES collaborated with two other organisations that provide support for families nationally.

One of these is *Mermaids*, which is a support group for children and teenagers coping with gender identity issues and their families. This charity provides a telephone helpline (07020 935066), e-mail contact *mermaids@freeuk.com* and website *http://www.mermaids.freeuk.com*.

The other organisation is *Depend*, a group supporting the families and friends of transsexual people via email *info@depend.org.uk* and a website *http://www.depend.org.uk*.

GIRES can also provide information about the local groups that support families in several areas of the UK. GIRES is willing to run further workshops wherever another organisation, such as a gender identity clinic, can assemble a group of family members.

LOCAL SUPPORT GROUPS

Local support groups for families have been set up in Southampton, Telford, Newcastle and Glasgow. Clearly, this provides incomplete coverage of the UK and many more groups are needed. GIRES strongly encourages other organisations to establish groups and can provide small amounts of funding to help them get started. However, experience shows that it is quite difficult to get the word out to families about the existence of the group, persuade them that it would be appropriate for them to attend and attract an adequate level of participation. Anyone attempting to start a group would have to put a lot of effort into publicising it. It can be promoted by contacting trans people themselves via the self-help groups, gender identity clinics, doctors and therapists that support them. However, the trans person may not pass on the invitation to the members of his or her family because they have not yet been told about the gender identity issues or because they have been told but, as happens far too often, have already rejected the trans person. So, the sponsors of support groups need to seek additional ways to get their message to the families, for instance via GPs' surgeries, therapists and counsellors, Samaritans, CABs and even advertising.

ROLE OF THE GENDER IDENTITY CLINICS

GIRES urges all Gender Identity Clinics to provide support for families.

Based on the comments of participants in the workshops, this should include:

1 Helping the gender dysphoric person to consider how best to preserve family relationships.
2 Talking with the family, rather than being remote.
3 With the consent of the gender dysphoric person, permitting other family members to attend at least one meeting with the supervising clinician.
4 Providing advice and information for family members.
5 Organising opportunities to meet other families.
6 Providing information on other sources of information and support.
7 Not using the family merely to check on what the gender dysphoric person has said.

8   Asking the trans person's workplace to explain gender dysphoria and transsexualism, thereby preventing the discrimination that too often ruins the lives of transsexual employees.

CONTACTING GIRES

GIRES will provide information and literature about gender dysphoria and transsexualism, their effects on family relationships, effective ways to support families and where to obtain other help. The charity can be contacted via: 01372 801554 Fax: 01372 272297, or e-mail: *admin@gires.org.uk* website: *http://www.gires.org.uk*

I am most grateful to The Trustees of GIRES for the Section above, particularly Terry and Bernard Reed.

With respect to some input on Terminology, I thank fellow Trustees of the Beaumont Trust, BM CHARITY LONDON WCIN 3XX

Website: *http://members.aol.com/Beaumonttrust*

Helpline 07000 287878 Tuesday & Thursday 7-11pm

FOR INFORMATION ABOUT NATIONAL AND LOCAL SUPPORT GROUPS PLEASE CONTACT THE BEAUMONT TRUST WEBSITE OR WRITE SENDING AN S.A.E.

73.   Post Script - Standard Care? A Counsellor's Overview.

Introduction.

It is not my intention here to challenge the Standards of Care in their new revised form. They have not yet been put into practice. Rather, it is to review the existing standard of care available this year in the U.K., as clients describe to me in my counselling practice and as people have described via the various helping networks. There are of course many satisfied customers.

However there also seem to be many who describe frustrations, distress and shortfalls in care. Many see themselves as survivors of the system of the care available rather than beneficiaries of it.

The Harry Benjamin International Gender Dysphoria Association's Standards of Care for Gender Identity Disorders were first adopted in original form in 1979. They are now, in 1998, in their fifth revision. Previous revisions were in 1980, 1981 and 1990.

There is no doubt that after nearly ten years, changes were overdue, not simply of these Standards, but in the spirit with which they were being interpreted and implemented by many clinics and private practitioners around the world.

In the early days of the Association mainly psychiatrists and surgeons operating in the U.S.A devised these Standards. These were to identify a set of diagnostic guidelines, a protocol and an appropriate treatment procedure, for those suffering from Gender Identity Conflict. Later this was termed "Transsexualism" and more recently "Gender Dysphoria". It should be noted that this protocol excludes intersexed people, although they too do actually have a gender identity, which may be in conflict with their assigned sex.

We owe a great deal to those early pioneers and particularly to Harry Benjamin himself. Before the Association was formed, individual practitioners worked in something of a vacuum, where danger lay for both the professional and the client. The professionals risked isolation or censure from others in the fields of Medicine, Surgery and Psychiatry and the law. Furthermore, practitioners in this pioneering field were also at risk of expensive litigation, particularly in the States, where any practitioner can be at extreme risk if found to be derelict in some way in treating a patient or client.

It always has been vital that terms and diagnoses be defined in such a way that this set of syndromes were both recognised and treated appropriately by medicine, so that specialist treatment could be provided within the aegis of Health Care systems. Prior to a working set of diagnoses, definitions and standards of care, most people suffering from these debilities were in much the same shocking position as hermaphrodites, on the sharp edge of the fence, getting the worst of both worlds.

It depended entirely on a few professionals interested in these matters as to whether any treatment be provided, and whether it was appropriately given. Their work was largely experimental and pioneering in the early days. Even today there are very many unanswered questions. There is still much need for research, evaluation and follow-up, quite apart from the ludicrous legal inequities, which remain.

Nineteenth century psychology offered little to this group of people who were placed by Freud, Ellis, Hirschfeld and others, in the same camp as homosexuals and were described as "inverts" or "perverts". These 'giants of psychology' were interested in sex, rather than in gender. Perhaps that is a price we have had to pay for having virtually exclusively male sex-researchers interested in these matters in post-Freudian Western Society.

As an aside, we are now hearing how Kinsey used material gathered by serial child molesters, as though it was valid science, disregarding the price in human suffering at the hands of these paedophiles. I find it tragic that a search for knowledge, which may be stimulated by acute testosterone poisoning in these great minds, seems to leave out the principal of care, which is of course traditionally feminine.

Those with gender identity issues were subjected to the same lack of compassion and censure, as were homosexuals by society, the law and by medicine. The problem was seen as entirely sexual, in terms of sexual preference, instead of as a matter of the gender identity of the individual. In some clinics treatment was denied to those MtF people who were not sexually attracted to men.

Great strides have been made, particularly in surgery, since the 1960's. Surgery was then far from perfect. Even now there is no way a reasonable erectile, sensile, phallus can be surgically constructed for the FtM's.

What support were gender dysphoric people given by religion, moral or ethical? A few, though not few enough, judgmental bigots from the vocal minority of the Judeo-Christian and Moslem religions with other moral pontificators then pitched in to add their weight to the guilt. They beat people up with bits of the Torah, the Old Testament or the Koran, in out-of-time and context quotes. This added to that pointing finger with which a bipolar society had already stabbed these people. The curious fact is that the Great Religions do not actually have any directive about gender identity, but zealots believe they are right and others wrong. They are dangerous and intolerant people who set themselves up as judge and jury.

It became a question of ethics in the context of prohibitions, instead of how ethically we can continue to avoid the fact that human beings are complex, and not simply male or female, masculine or feminine, only preferring a partner of the opposite sex/gender.

229

Labels and Difference:

No distinction exists in the vocabularies and the minds of many people between sex and gender. A lack of semantic clarity adds to this stress. It is time to athetise, by this I mean invalidate, such misuse of our language. Language is a form of communication and sadly we all seem to use words in different ways. It is vital that we use terms, which are understood and defined. Words can be used to liberate or to trap us.

Against this it is also important that we, having devised a name, a diagnosis, term or label, like "transsexual", need to see the person and not the label.

As a nurse I hope I was not too guilty of seeing "the appendectomy in bed three - to be given a premed' after she is in her gown", instead of seeing Jane, an old lady who is frightened and bewildered by what is about to happen to her in theatre. Personally, I see labels as a helpful shorthand, but they do over simplify and tend to marginalise people. Each of us is a person in her or his own right and deserves respect. Gays, through the pink-pound and gay-power and an evolving, slightly less intolerant society, have effected improvements in public attitudes and the legal system. Here in Great Britain there is no effective lilac-pound or trannie-power, and I am not sure we would want even more martyrs to the cause. Isn't it time to invite society, medicine and its Standards of Care, the Law and the Churches to get real?

We are not only dealing with a life enhancing or threatening situation but with simple human dignity.

A bipolar society which fails to benefit from the actual reality and richness of experience of those who have really examined who and what they are, is in danger of losing the possibly liberating cultural balance brought about by the presence of all the exceptions to so-called "normality".

When we see normality as including difference, and that as a richness, instead of a challenge to wobbly notions of what 'should' be, humanity might have freed itself from the tyranny of Predeterminism (genetic, Darwinian or social). Then we may approach something resembling the wisdom with which Homo 'sapiens', as our species has named itself. Meanwhile "Homo bipolaris" might be a more apt term to use for our species.

If we see an albino blackbird hounded to death by its peers, we understand a little of the 'natural' fear of difference. But let us realise how much we have benefited from the vast numbers of types of animals, which have been bred and selected because of particular features, or qualities they possess which are of benefit to us. Society itself needs to evolve into something with a more humanistic and open attitude to difference and to the possibilities afforded by the fact that identity is such a complex feature of any individual.

Society need not be a force for oppression, but liberation, if it recognises the individual. Evolution itself occurs because variations, which are themselves natural, are selected. I wonder how long a poodle would last in the wild? Perhaps better than a transsexual in a crowd full of lads, or someone trying to fit in with Standards of Care which may be badly applied and be set in concrete.

To make the patient fit the diagnosis is not only unrealistic but poor medicine. However without a diagnosis, treatment can only be a shot in the dark for both clinician and patient.

Treating the Individual.

Why not an individual person-centred holistic approach?

The revised 1998 SOC say that these standards allow for clinical departures from these guidelines *"because of a patients unique anatomic, social or psychological situation."*

This gives hope towards a more person-centred approach. They go on to suggest that usually *"the FtM seems to be further along in his consolidating a male gender identity, than the MtF usually is in her quest towards a comfortable female identity."*

I feel that although it is clear that statistically the FtM presents on average earlier than the MtF, the reason for the clinician's cautions may be that they are men. The MtF is joining the wrong side, and may be judged as women often are, on criteria of appearance rather than identity. I simply state a caution here.

In the widest sense of medicine, many of the attitudes of professionals, who we might hope know better, seem to be outdated, bipolar and restricted. Doctors of medicine have far too little time during training devoted to issues of sex or gender or psychology. Interestingly the gender dysphoric person by her or his dilemma is in fact responding to bipolarity, towards the pole to which she or he feels he or she belongs.

The brain itself appears to be gendered, so perhaps it is not altogether surprising that this sense of bipolarity encourages a certain rigidity both in the client and the professional carer. For this reason it is important that the Standards be flexible and more person-centred.

Clinicians are busy people, but it is vital that they see patients as individuals and treat them holistically instead of simply by the book or worse arbitrarily.

In psychological terms there are often hangovers of this simplistic and patriarchal, sexual-Freudian overview still held by many first-line practitioners and the general public, which only adds to the confusion and suffering of the gender dysphoric person and those around her or him. The unenlightened treatment by the law and much of media exposure of this subject only adds to this distress. Sadly this type of thinking still persists among some medical professionals. To many a G.P. the workings of the human mind are too arcane for consideration.

Purpose of Standards of Care:

The purpose of the Standards of Care (SOC) *(here I quote from the 1998 draft) is to articulate the HBIGDA's International *"professional consensus about the psychiatric, psychological, medical and surgical management of Gender Identity disorders."*

We are told that the Treatment Goal *"is that the specific psychotherapeutic, endocrine or surgical therapies for people with gender identity disorders is lasting personal comfort with the gendered self, in order to maximise overall psychological well-being and self-fulfilment."*

The SOC is clinical guidelines and is *"to provide flexible directions for the treatment of gender identity disorders."*

Management as a Rigid Process.

The keyword in providing effective Standards of Care here is flexible. If a goal is to help provide people with gender identity disorders with lasting personal comfort with the gendered-self to maximise overall psychological well-being and self-fulfilment, why one wonders do some G.I.C's seem to encourage or sustain such an adversarial and unsympathetic ethos?

As a counsellor I see clients who seem often more distressed than helped by their visits to a G.I.C. Whilst it is true that challenges are a worthwhile way of helping to find an unguarded truth perhaps, I have the impression that many seem to have found each of their visits to a G.I.C. one in which they found trauma rather than comfort.

I have the impression there are checklists of questions put to clients in a way, which they found to be offensive or even destructive.

I do not believe that two or three hour's psychiatric assessment over a year spent attending a Clinic can do other than monitor a patient. Frankly there seems to be no psychotherapy or counselling offered to most gender dysphoric persons. Therapy seems to consist of the administration of hormones, if they are deemed suitable, and monitoring and assessing suitability for surgery.

Equally there are concerns that those who take the option of private medicine may run the risk of being too precipitous, if they are not also helped with appropriate trained counselling or psychotherapy. Further there are those who we all have met who have not spent time adjusting to their actual gender who get surgery too soon, or even inappropriately, simply because they can provide the finances to do so and they have made the right noises to their psychiatrists.

There do need to be cautions in the private sector. I have met several post-op transvestites, whose surgery was more about the clothes they like to wear, rather than because they are gendered females. Transvestites are well advised to become at ease about their cross-dressing, and not to use Transsexuality as a way past guilt-feelings about being a cross-dresser.

There are also concerns for the FtM's that generally do not have financial resources as many of the MtF's to bypass over long waiting lists for their surgical confirmation.

Frequently the MtF's go to a National Health G.I.C. for hormones, but faced with long waiting lists and an unempathetic G.I.C., get their surgery privately. Who can blame them? What happens to the people who do not have funds available? A two-tier system has evolved; leaving much of the frustration and tears for those who need most help from the Health Service.

Management as Monitoring:

Management seems to be a process of monitoring with little or no therapy provided, which clients describe as a series of hoops through which they have to pass, rather like an uncomfortable rite of passage.

Networks.

There is a lot of pain, confusion, loneliness and isolation as well as discrimination and bigotry in law and society. This experience often extends to include parents and partners in a climate where sexual or gender confusion is considered a bad joke rather than being addressed with compassion and practical solutions and acceptance.

Let us hope the new SOC go some way towards this, and there seems to be a better future if the philosophy behind these standards be implemented in the G.I.C.'s and by private practitioners.

The **GENDYS Network** has a heart as well as a head. We hope the ideal of real care will be promoted by ourselves. We include hermaphrodites, transgenderists, transhomosexuals, partners, parents, in fact all types of people as equal members of the Network, as well as caring professionals specialising in this type of work and interested in the debates of gender and sexuality.

We have as goals tolerance and understanding.

We see the benefits of Counselling and Psychotherapy as greatly underestimated or ignored by the current Gender Clinics. Sadly the role of support groups seems greatly underestimated by both the SOC and the GIC's. Such groups as ours can be a resource to the patients of the overworked and underfunded clinicians.

There are many situations that are far worse than being transexed, but a debt of gratitude is owed to those who have helped.

The main aim of this book was to inform people affected by the Trans situation, and to help professionals in the field have some understanding of this phenomenon.

There is also a plea for an improved standard of care and that the Standards of Care adopted in this country are person-centred, flexible and are guidelines, rather than devised simply to ensure the professionals avoid litigation.

Informed Consent is essential, with water tight Consent forms, so that a patient takes full personal responsibility for any therapy or surgery she or he embarks on … That is why counselling is essential.

The reason I have spelt Trans-Exed this way is because after things are resolved the individual is Ex Trans, is simply a woman or a man with a history … Not A Trans-Sexual!

We all have an inner life. Humans have several dimensions and are not simply our bodies, our sex or our gender.

The power of the mind is to enable a prisoner to travel the world, without moving, or to feel imprisoned when there is no door. Even a crippled person can dance through the Universe and hear the harmony of the music of the Stars.

As I have said before, we are all made of stardust.

For information about the Gendys Network,
please write, enclosing an s.a.e., to
BM GENDYS,
London WC1N 3XX

74.   Bibliography and Further Reading.

Many of the books listed may not now be in publication. Ask at your local library to see 'Whitaker's Books in Print'.

Archer and Lloyd (1982) *Sex and Gender,* Penguin   ISBN 0 14 022194 8

Jo Durden-Smith (1983) *Sex and the Brain,* Pan   ISBN 0 330 28036 8

Harry Benjamin Gender Dysphoria Assn Inc. *Standards of Care* various editions

Harry Benjamin (1966) *The Transsexual Phenomenon,* Julian Press

E. Berne (1973) *What Do You Say After You Say Hello?* Bantam

Jed Bland (1994) *The Gender Paradox,* Derby TV/TS Group.
                                                    ISBN 0 9517885 2 3

Jed Bland (ed) (2004) *Transvestism and Cross Dressing - Current Views,* Beaumont Trust.   ISBN 0 9521357 6 0

W.R. Bion (1962) *Learning from Experience* Heinemann

W. Bockting and E.Coleman (1992) *Gender Dysphoria Inter-disciplinary Approaches in Clinical Management,* Hawthorn   ISBN 1 56024 473 9

D. Brown and J. Pedder (1979) *Introduction to Psychotherapy,* Routledge
                                                    ISBN 0 415 04547 9

David Cauldwell (1965) *Transvestism* Sexology Corp (NY)

Council of Europe Proceedings XX111 Colloquy on European Law, (1995) Vrije Universiteit Amsterdam 14-16 April 1993 Council of Europe Pubs   ISBN 92 871 2805 7

Pasteur Douce, (1986) *La Question Transsexuelle,* Lumiere et Justice
                                                    ISBN 2 906033 01 4

Windy Dryden (1992) *Brief Counselling,* Open University Press
                                                    ISBN 0335 09972 6

Windy Dryden (1984) *Individual Therapy in Britain,* Open University Press   ISBN 0 335 09810 X

R.V.Kraft Ebbing *Psychopathia Sexualis,* Heinemann

A. Ellis (1979) *Theoretical and Empirical Foundations of Rational Emotive Therapy,* Brooks/Cole Baltimore

Havelock Ellis *Studies in the Psychology of Sex Vol. VII - Eonism*

Gerard Egan (1985) *The Skilled Helper,* Brooks Cole
                                                    ISBN 0 534 05904 X

Julia Epstein (ed) (1991) *Body Guards: The Cultural Politics of Gender Ambiguity,* Routledge ISBN 0 415 90389 0

E. Erikson (1965) *Childhood and Society*, Penguin

E. Erikson *The problem of Ego Identity*, Jnl. Am. Psy'anal'Assn..4.56-121.

H. J. Eyseneck *Fact and Fiction in Psychology* Penguin ISBN 0 1402 0696 5

Leslie Feinberg (1998) *Transgender Warriors*, Beacon Books
ISBN 0 8070 7940 5

Deborah Fienbloom (1977) *Transvestites and Transsexuals*, Delta Publs
ISBN 0 440 58996 7

Sigmund Freud *Complete Psychological Works*, Hogarth Press

Louis Gooren (1991) *What do we Know About the Biology of Gender Dysphoria?* 10th World Congress for Sexuality Amsterdam

Richard Green (1974) *Sexual Identity Conflict*, Duckworth
ISBN 0 7156 0774 X

Richard Green and John Money (1969) *Transsexualism and Sex Reassignment*, Johns Hopkins Press   ISBN 0 8018 1038 8

Richard Green (1974) *Sexual Identity Conflict in Children and Adults*, Penguin   ISBN 0 1400 3957 0

R. Greenson (1967) *The Technique and Practice of Psychoanalysis*, Hogarth

Harrington, *Male and Female Identity*, Wiley

Michael Haslam (1978) *Sexual Disorders*, Pitman,   ISBN 0 272 79508 9

Michael Haslam (1993) *Transvestism*, Beaumont Trust
ISBN 0 9521357 0 1

Magnus Hirschfeld (1938) *Sexual Anomalies and Perversions*, Encyclopaedic Press

Liz Hodgkinson (1987) *Bodyshock*, Gurnsey Press   ISBN 0 86287 317 7

Lunde Holt et al, *Fundamentals of Human Sexuality*

Johnson and Brown (1982) *The Gender Trap - TS Parents*, Proteus
ISBN 0 906071 54 2

Carl Jung (1933) *Modern Man in Search of a Soul*, Routledge

B Kamprad (1991) *Het Verkeerde Lichaam Alles Over Transseksuliteit*, Ambo   ISBN 90 263 12023

R. Karim (1996) *Vaginoplasty in Transsexuals*, VU Press Amsterdam
ISBN 90 5383 496 6

Jacques Lacan *The Four Fundamental Concepts of Psycho-analysis*, Peregrine

A. Levitsky and Perls (1972) *The Rules and Games of Gestalt Therapy*, Charles Merrill

Lundstrom, *Gender Dysphoria*, Gotenborg

Marmor, (1965) *Sexual Inversion*, Basic Books

Juliet Mitchel *A Selected Melanie Klein*, Penguin   ISBN 0 14 013730 0

John Money (1972) *Man and Woman - Boy and Girl*, J. Hopkins Uni.
Press   ISBN 0 8018 1405 7

John Money (1975) *Sexual Signatures - on Being a Man or a Woman*,
Harrap   ISBN 0245 52954 3

Stephen Murgatroyd (1985) *Counselling and Helping*, Routledge
ISBN 0 901715 41 70

Sherry Ortner (1981) *Sexual Meanings The Cultural Construction of Gender
and Society*, Cambridge Uni. Press   ISBN 0 521 23965 6

Frederik Perls (1973) *Gestalt Therapy*, Penguin   ISBN 0 285 62665 5

Quilliam and Grove Stephensen, *Best Counselling Guide*, Thorsons
Publishing Group

Janice Raymond (1979) *The Transsexual Empire*, The Woman's Press

Carl Rogers (1965) *Client Centred Therapy*, Redwood Press
ISBN 0 09 45399 0

Carl Rogers (1967) *On Becoming a Person*, Constable ISBN 0 09 454020 9

Joan Roughgarden (2004) *Evolution's Rainbow*, Uni Cal Press
ISBN 0 520 24073 1

E. de Savitch, (1958) *Homosexuality and Transexuality*, Heinemann

Schutz (1967) *Joy, Expanding Human Awareness*, Grove Press

Martin Stanton (1983) *Outside the Dream, Lacan and French Styles of
Psychoanalysis*, Routledge   ISBN 0 7100 9273 3

Robert Stoller (1968) *Sex and Gender on the Development of Masculinity and
Femininity*, Hogarth   ISBN 0 7012 0321 8

Robert Stoller (1975) *The Transsexual Experiment*, Hogarth
ISBN 0 7012 0400 1

Rose Tremain (1992) *Sacred Country*, Sinclair   ISBN 1 85619 118 4

Bryan Tully (1992) *Accounting for Transsexualism and Transhomosexuality*,
Whiting and Birch   ISBN 1 871177 04 9

Walinder, (1967) *Transexualism*, Gotenborg

C. Whitfield (1989) *Healing the Child Within*, Health Communications
Inc   ISBN 0 932194 40 0

A. Woodhouse, *Fantastic Women*, Macmillan

Biography.

April Ashley's Odyssey, 1982, Cape   ISBN 0224 01849 3

The Transvestite Memoires of the Abbe De Choisy, 1973, ScottOwen
      ISBN 0 7206 0122 3

Memoires- M. L'Abbe De Choisy Habille en Femme, Mercure De France,
1966

Caroline Cossey - My Story, Faber   ISBN 0 571 16251 7

Roberta Cowell's Story, Heinemann 1954

Michael nee Laura, Michael Dillon

Memoires of the Chevalier D'Eon, Trans Antonia White, Blond,1970

L'Etrange Destinee du Chevalier D'Eon, Pierre Pinsseau, Paris1944

Le Chevalier D'Eon, G Melinand Profidou, Paris 1979

(Lili Elbe) Man into Woman, Ed Niels Hoyer, Jarrolds 1933

(Lili Elbe) Man into Woman, 2004 Blue Boat Books,
      ISBN 0 9547072 9 6

J. Fry, *Being Different,* Wiley

(Julia Grant) *Just Julia* and *Just Julia* 1980, New Eng. Library
      ISBN 0 450 04715

Christine Jorgensen - a Personal Autobiography, Erikson Inc
      LOC NO 67-21524 1967

Maud Marin, *Le saut de l'ange,* 1987, Fixot   ISBN 9 782876 450011

Morgan, P., *Man Maid Doll,* Lyle Stuart

(Jan Morris) *Conundrum.* 1974, Faber   ISBN 0 571 10337 5

Zachary Nataf *Lesbians Talk Transgender,* 1996, Scarlet Press
      ISBN 1 85727 008 8

Mark Rees *Dear Sir or Madam,* 1996, Cassell   ISBN 0 304 33398 4

D.L.Simmons, D.L., *Man into Woman,* Icon Books

G.Turtle, *A Girl Called Georgina,* The Book Guild

Also by the Author.

Alice Purnell, (1990/95) *A Guide to Transsexualism, Transgenderism and
Gender Dysphoria,* Gender Trust Pubs,   ISBN 1 873049 01 03

Alice Purnell, (1998) *A Guide to Transsexualism, Transgenderism and
Gender Dysphoria,* Gendys Conferences,   ISBN 0 9525107 2 3

Conference Papers

1990: *It's all in the Mind,* GENDYS International Gender Dysphoria Conference,   British Library catalogue reference 4096.401960 DSC

1992: *An Assessment of Treatments and Follow-up of 102 Transsexuals* GENDYS II, The Second International Gender Dysphoria Conference,   British Library catalogue reference YK.1994.b.14220

1994: *Gender counselling, and its difficulties in cases of acute and chronic gender dysphoria.* GENDYS '94, The Third International Gender Dysphoria Conference,   ISBN 0 9525107 0 7

1996: *Fifty Plus Survey* GENDYS '96, The Fourth International Gender Dysphoria Conference,   ISBN 0 9525107 1 5

1997: *Some of the Effects of Those who have Various Relationships with Gender Dysphoric People,* Northern Gender Dysphoria Conference Conf Report Ed. J. Gilmore

1998: *Standard Care? A Counsellor's overview.* GENDYS '98, The Fifth International Gender Dysphoria Conference,   ISBN 09525107 3 1

2000: *The Client Leads in Effective Gender Counselling,* GENDYS 2k, The Sixth International Gender Dysphoria Conference,   ISBN 0 9525107 4 X

2002: *Difference and the Existential a Positive View,* GENDYS 2002, The Seventh International Gender Dysphoria Conference,   ISBN 09525107 5 8

2003: *Gender Variations Self Esteem in a Critical Society,* Transgender 2003 Conference, Univ. of E Anglia Conf Report CD Rom.

2004: *Non Stereotypical Adjustment is Important for a Complete Personality - Be Yourself,* GENDYS 2002, The Eighth International Gender Dysphoria Conference,   ISBN 0 9525107 6 6

Details of how to obtain copies of the above publications are obtainable on sending an s.a.e. requesting these from the GENDYS NETWORK, BM GENDYS, London WC1N 3XX.

Poetry.

Bad Timing, 1988, Pub Limited Company
Sex and Chocolate, 1989, Page Four
I Wet Myself, 1999, Golden Flower Press   ISBN 1 873049 02 1